Semmelweis,
The Conqueror of Childbed Fever

FRANK G. SLAUGHTER, M.D.

SEMMELWEIS,

OF

THE CONQUEROR CHILDBED FEVER

COLLIER BOOKS

NEW YORK, N.Y.

Semmelweis, The Conqueror of Childbed Fever, originally appeared under the title *Immortal Magyar*.

This Collier Books edition is published by arrangement with Abelard-Schuman Ltd.

Collier Books is a division of The Crowell-Collier Publishing Company.

First Collier Books Edition 1961

Foreword

IN PREPARING this biography of Dr. Ignaz Philipp Semmelweis for the general reader, I have drawn freely upon a great number of references concerning him, both in book and journal form, to which I acknowledge my indebtedness. The basic biography in English, and an invaluable source in this book, is *Semmelweis: His Life and His Doctrine,* by Sir William J. Sinclair (Manchester, at the University Press, 1909). Basic biographies in German are those of Fritz Schürer von Waldheim (1905), Jacob Bruck (1887), and Alfred Hegar (1882), all of which have furnished material for this biography. Dr. Tiberius von Gyory of Budapest published in 1905 the collected works of Semmelweis.

No bibliography is appended to this book, but the interested reader is referred to the exhaustive bibliography by Dr. Frank P. Murphy, published in the *Bulletin of the History of Medicine* (Vol. XX, No. 5, December, 1946). The many quotations which I have given from Semmelweis' own book, *Die Ætiologie,* are from the translation of that work by Dr. Frank P. Murphy, published in *Medical Classics* (Vol. V, Nos. 5-8, 1941), and have been used with Dr. Murphy's permission. He has also been kind enough to read and comment upon this manuscript.

I am also indebted to Miss Lora Frances Davis, Librarian for the Florida State Board of Health, to Miss Audrey Broward, Reference Librarian of the Jacksonville Public Library, and to Mrs. A. S. Limouze, who has contributed no little by editing this manuscript.

Frank G. Slaughter, M.D.

Contents

Chapter 1

The Setting

IN VIENNA in 1847 an obscure Hungarian, Ignaz Philipp Semmelweis, found the solution to a problem which had vexed medical men for centuries. And after this discovery he devoted his life to convincing mankind of its truth, with indifferent success. This is the story of his painstaking search, of his struggle for recognition, of his bitter defeat and death.

Semmelweis sought the cause of puerperal fever, a terrible disease which ravaged the lying-in hospitals of his time, killing thousands of mothers and often their new-born babies. The disease had been known since ancient times, at first as simply an occasional complication at childbirth. During the seventeenth, eighteenth, and nineteenth centuries, with the crowding of population into cities and the charitable establishment of hospitals in which the poor could bear their children, puerperal fever grew to be a pestilence. Between the years 1652 and 1862 there were two hundred so-called epidemics of the disease. Perhaps the most severe of these epidemics began in 1773, killing more than a tenth of the population of the lying-in hospitals of Europe and raging for three years. In Lombardy, it was reported, for more than a year no woman survived childbirth.

One thing characterized these epidemics: they occurred in hospitals. In 1646, for example, the disease appeared in the great Paris hospital, the Hôtel Dieu, attacking more than a tenth of the occupants and killing almost every one. Conditions in the Hôtel Dieu were on a par with those in other great charity hospitals of the period: filth was everywhere; a half dozen or more patients, sick from various causes, lay in the same bed; freshly delivered mothers were placed beside those dying from infection; bodies cold in death sometimes stayed for twenty-four hours beside those consumed by raging fevers. Such a shocking picture seems incredible to us now, but it was the rule then, rather than the exception. Under such conditions it is not surprising that pestilences raged, nor that childbed fever was among the most virulent.

But even in hospitals where conditions were better than the Hôtel Dieu—admittedly the worst—the childbed fever also raged. About 1750 the first lying-in hospital was established in the British Isles and in the same year puerperal fever broke out in London, killing twenty-four women in less than six months. The famed Lying-in Hospital in Dublin was not immune, and after the disease appeared there in 1767, repeated epidemics occurred. Next to be involved were the maternity wards of Edinburgh; the pestilence swept through them, leaving the wards almost empty. In Aberdeen, a great epidemic raged in 1793, so intense that it even attacked women delivered in their homes, a rare occurrence before that time.

Elsewhere in Europe the story was the same, with one in five mothers dying in the Allmänna Barnbördshuset of Stockholm, and all hospitals of Paris losing one in every nineteen. Even in Vienna, already becoming a center of medical knowledge, the fever raged. In the Allgemeine Krankenhaus, famed hospital established by Joseph II and one of the leading institutions of its kind in the world, the story was the same, or worse. An epidemic beginning in 1822 killed one mother in every six.

In America childbed fever was far from unknown, but since hospitals had reached no such high degree of development as in Europe, there were fewer opportunities for infection. Throughout the world, however, there seemed to be a slowly smoldering bed of fever, waiting to break into flame at any time and yield a harvest of maternal death and sorrow.

Puerperal fever, popularly called "childbed fever," is, as we now know, not a disease in its own right, but simply a form of septicemia. The dread streptococcus, which causes such diseases as "strep" throat, scarlet fever, and rheumatic fever, is responsible also for this mortal illness of child-bearing women. If we cut a finger and it becomes infected, the surrounding area turns red, swells, and becomes painful. Severe infections result in a spread through the lymphatic channels of the arm, with red streaks running up the arms, fever, delirium, and a dangerous condition, medically called septicemia, popularly "blood poisoning," which often results in death. With true septicemia the infection spreads into the body, causing involvement of the brain, the lungs, the abdomen, and other vital organs.

Puerperal fever, so called from *puerperium,* the term for the period immediately following childbirth, is just such an infection, beginning inside the "womb," or uterus. Germs, usually the streptococcus, reach the uterus from various causes—dirty hands, dirty instruments, prolonged labor, with many examinations. There they enter the wound, the raw inner surface of the uterus, from which the placenta or "after-birth" has been detached at the end of the delivery. In such a fertile bed, bacteria multiply and spread rapidly, first involving the uterus itself, then the organs of the abdomen, later the whole body. The picture is exactly the same as that from "blood poisoning" due to any other cause: fever, chills, delirium; the difference lies merely in where the germs enter the body.

Fortunately, germs do not normally ascend the birth passage following delivery of the child, so long as they are not introduced there in some way. Primitive women had little childbed fever, for this dread affliction is actually a product of civilization. In Biblical times there were strict laws about the care of woman in labor, laws which also served in many ways to protect her against infection. And during the Middle Ages, women were still delivered of their offspring in their homes, with little interference and little infection. But the establishment of great hospitals and even the evolution of improved obstetrical techniques led inevitably to the increase of infectious diseases.

The primitive woman whose baby was presented in an abnormal position, transversely or feet first, usually died, and her child with her, or the child alone was removed by a mutilating operation. In the sixteenth century the famous surgeon Ambroise Paré re-introduced podalic version, a method of turning the child in the uterus before birth. And in the same century and the following, successive members of the Chamberlen family were famed for a secret method which they used in delivering difficult births. Divulged after two centuries by a member of the family, the secret consisted of a pair of forceps, which soon became a popular instrument with "man-midwives."

Both these techniques entailed active interference in the process of birth and direct invasion of the birth passage. And, in the total ignorance of antisepsis, the examining hand or assisting instrument was naturally seldom above reproach. Physicians conveyed infection to their private patients and in the great hospitals, midwives, doctors, and students went from patient to patient carrying death on their hands. What wonder that puerperal fever soon became a major scourge of womankind.

The history of the fight against the scourge of puerperal infection is, viewed from our present perspective, but part of a larger history, that of the development of antiseptic science. Surgery came into its own place in medicine through the discovery of methods of *antisepsis,* that is, the use of chemicals to destroy infection which was already present. The ultimate end of such progress, of course, was *asepsis,* the killing of all germs before they can come in contact with the wound, through sterilization of everything which is a potential source of infection.

Obstetrics is in a way a form of surgery, especially in modern practice, when most first deliveries, at least, are accompanied by the making of an incision called an *episiotomy.* The same rules prevail to prevent infection in obstetrics as in surgery; the infection, if it develops, differs only in its locale. The rigid surgical technique to which we are so accustomed today had no counterpart before Lister's use of antisepsis in 1865. His method was the forerunner of our modern principles of asepsis.

Hospitals of the sixteenth to nineteenth centuries were as bad in their surgical wards as they were in their obstetrical ones, and infection was equally prevalent in both. In most hospitals there was little choice between the two departments, but while surgical patients could avoid infection by refusing to be operated upon, the mother who had reached her time could not prevent the birth of her child, with all of its dangerous consequences.

Surgical wards were crowded, filthy, poorly ventilated. Surgeons operated—when they operated at all—in old coats, stained with blood and pus from hundreds of wounds, their hands often went unwashed from one operation to the next. The patients lay under the perpetual threat of infection, either from the surgeon's hands and those of the attendants or from the uncleanness of their linens and other surroundings. Erysipelas, septicemia, pyemia, and gangrene stalked the wards, claiming their victims. The danger of infection severely limited the scope of surgery. Accidents requiring amputation, wounds requiring dressing, abscesses to be opened, these constituted the major portion of surgical practice. Any surgeon who had the temerity to venture into the abdomen, the chest, or the brain expected not only to lose his patient, but also to incur the severe criticism of his colleagues.

The solution of the problem of surgical infection, as well

as puerperal infection, awaited the development of a knowledge of the source of wound infection, and this knowledge was to be amassed by the great bacteriologists of the nineteenth century. Far earlier, however, the groundwork had been laid.

Since earliest times man has been concerned with wounds and their effects. Infection and suppuration were generally expected in wounds and were taken as a matter of course. The Greek physicians, however, used wine (alcohol is an excellent antiseptic) and other dressings which undoubtedly had great antiseptic value. They sutured wounds and obtained a surprisingly good state of healing, sometimes without infection.

Galen, the famous second-century physician, is given credit for the concept of "laudable pus," the phrase used for the ordorless, creamy pus that surgeons hoped to find in healing wounds. He did have great success in treating the wounds of gladiators and with his medical knowledge, advanced for his day, it is hardly to be expected that he would actually say that pus should develop in wounds in order for them to heal well. Whether he stated it or not, the concept that inflammation and "laudable pus" should be present for a wound to heal properly persisted until relatively modern times and held back surgical progress for many centuries.

Theodoric, Bishop of Cervia, attacked the "laudable pus" theory in 1266, in a surgical treatise, surprisingly modern in its concepts for all that it was written six hundred years before Semmelweis and Lister. His treatment was simple: leave wounds alone and keep them dry. Unfortunately, Guy de Chauliac (1300-67), most eminent surgeon of medieval times, revived the "laudable pus" concept during the fourteenth and fifteenth centuries.

Next to suggest simplicity in wound treatment was Paracelsus (1490-1541), often credited with being the "most original thinker of the sixteenth century." Daring in most of his medical concepts, he taught that wounds did best when let alone, but Paracelsus had a faculty for making enemies, perhaps because he did not know the meaning of tact. Still another sixteenth century physician, Fracastorius (1483-1553), published in 1546 a treatise called *De Contagione,* in which he described methods of infection and even mentioned imperceptible *seminaria,* or seeds, which he said transmitted disease.

In 1684 Francesco Redi (1626-98) refuted one of the great credos of medieval science, that of the spontaneous generation of visible creatures. And Anthony van Leeuwenhoeck (1632-1723), the first great scientist of the microscope, discovered and described bacteria on September 17, 1683, paving the way for Pasteur's later discoveries.

In the eighteenth century, Sir John Pringle and Madame d'Arconville investigated the process of putrefaction and, without discovering its cause, established the value of various antiseptic substances in delaying the process. In 1810 a French confectioner, Nicholas Appert, published an account of his method of preserving food by excluding air and applying heat, and thus laid the foundation for the modern canning industry. In 1819 Labarraque made the first solution of chlorine for purposes of disinfecting, and William Street suggested the sterilization of supplies and equipment with dry heat.

Thus, by the time of Semmelweis in the mid-nineteenth century, these workers and others, following devious paths, had brought men close to the realization that fermentation and putrefaction, whether in foods or in human wounds, were the work of living organisms borne in the air, organisms destructible by heat and by various chemical substances. The destructive techniques were, in fact, better known that the nature of the thing destroyed. And that, unfortunately, was the stumbling block which held back progress for a long time.

The final revelation, the fact that the universe around us teems with microscopic life, both beneficial and harmful, was made while Semmelweis still lived, by the great Louis Pasteur, when he announced in 1857 that "fermentation is correlative with life." In 1864 he finally refuted the theory of spontaneous generation. And the value of Pasteur's discoveries to surgery was to be realized in the year of Semmelweis' death by Joseph Lister, who founded the technique of antiseptic surgery on the principle that putrefaction is caused by microorganisms constantly present in the air and can be prevented by the destruction of these organisms before, and sometimes after, they have entered a wound.

In this great story of a life-saving principle, the puerperal-fever fight waged by Semmelweis and his predecessors strikes a curiously anticipatory note. For these men to some extent used Lister's means without possessing Lister's knowledge. They evolved methods of preventing streptococci from attacking mothers without actually knowing what they were preventing. They acted upon theories largely fallacious—and Semmelweis was as much in error as any other—to achieve an end that harmonized with the unknown facts.

Chapter 2

Youth and Study

VIENNA, 1837.

Vienna, capital of pleasure, proud center of a dying empire, repeating tales of a glory long past and eagerly anticipating a future when the world should once more bow down to the Hapsburgs—a future that was not to be. In the Glacis, beautiful women walked in the sunshine, glancing demurely upward into the admiring eyes of officers in brilliant uniforms. And in the coffee-houses diplomats gathered over their cups, fencing warily for each other's secrets. Over the scene poured brilliant sunlight and the liquid, swaying waltzes of the older Strauss.

Behind this gay scene, the forces of unrest were at work. Only two years before, the death of Emperor Francis I—"unser Kaiser Franz"—had robbed the empire of a greatly beloved ruler, conscientious though indolent, enlightened but conservative. Ferdinand, his son and successor, was a mere child in politics, never the strong man needed to restore the failing empire. The great chancellor Metternich, who might have accomplished the task, was hampered by enemies and court intrigue. He labored futilely while the central organization of the state fell into rapid decline. All the while, Prussia to the north, a stalwart youth in the congress of nations, was feeling in its muscles the growing strength which, thirty years later, was to humble Austria into the dust of Königgrätz.

In the cafes of the Josephstadt students laughed and drank with the exuberant spirits of youth. Near by rose the massive buildings of the University of Vienna and the famed Allgemeine Krankenhaus, the General Hospital. The squat, barrack-like structure of the hospital had been built in 1784 in honor of the empress, Maria Theresa, and medical history was made within its walls with each succeeding year. The men who walked its dingy halls were preoccupied by an intense search for facts, for concrete knowledge, and the dissecting knife saw greater use than the surgeon's scalpel. The creed of academic life in Vienna was pronounced by Professor Dietl when he said: "Our ancestors laid much stress on the success of their treatment of the sick; we, however, on the result of our investigations. Our tendency is purely scientific. The physician should be judged by the extent of his knowledge and not by the number of his cures. It is the investigator, not the healer, that is to be appreciated in the physician."

Often to be found at the tables in the students' coffeehouses was a young Hungarian, just turned nineteen, Ignaz Philipp Semmelweis. Born on the first of July, 1818, Semmelweis was the fourth child of a shopkeeper of Ofen or Buda. Though wholly Hungarian, he was German in ancestry; generations before, the astute Austrian rulers of Hungary had welcomed German colonists into the country to act as a leaven to the rebellious Magyar spirit.

Ignaz's father, Joseph Semmelweis, carried on a moderately profitable business; his wife, Therese Müller Semmelweis, the daughter of a merchant, was incessantly occupied with the concerns of a rapidly growing family.

Young Semmelweis had received an elementary education of sorts in the primary school and the Gymnasium of Buda. He was apparently a good scholar, a lively and clever boy, with a ready tongue and an active imagination. But Hungarian schools in that day were deficient in many respects. The teaching of language, in particular, was neglected or mishandled. In consequence Semmelweis had difficulty throughout life in expressing himself in writing: to write meant for him a bitter struggle with grammar, punctuation, and spelling. Hence perhaps came the "inborn antipathy to all that is called writing," which he later gave as the reason for his long delay in presenting his great doctrine to the world. An additional source of confusion in his schooling was the existence of two folkspeeches, German and Hungarian, both of which he learned, neither well. His speech, as well as his writing, was therefore rather impaired than improved by his instructors.

The defectiveness of his education was, however, in one sense a blessing to Semmelweis, for neither the years at the Gymnasium nor the two (1835-1837) which he spent as a student of "philosophy" at the University of Pest so crammed him with knowledge as to inhibit his power to think for himself. When he went to Vienna in the autumn of 1837, he was fresh of mind and spirit, full of curiosity and enthusiasm, ready to strike out in his own search for truth, in blithe independence of authority. The quiet and reserved manner which had grown upon him with the coming of adolescent self-consciousness was softened by a look of honest kindliness, which could change at once to honest indignation when his sense of truth and rightness was offended.

Parental ambition, however, had set a course for him in which his independent mind could bring him only trouble. He was destined to become an auditing clerk, employed in settling the many disputes which arose between the armies of Austria and the people over whose lands they moved. In the fall of 1837 he had enrolled in the law school of the University of Vienna and begun his studies, but the work had no charms for him. His heart was not in the dusty tomes containing the myriad decrees which "Our Good Kaiser Franz" had promulgated to guide the footsteps of his subjects and to build up the intricate bureaucracy which ruled Austria. The young man could hope some day, after spending a few years following the armies in the position of advocate, to occupy one of the lesser government positions; he might even one day fill a responsible office and take his place in a stratum of society only one step below the court.

These prospects were not sufficient, however, to reconcile young Semmelweis to the dull study of law, and he found it more to his taste to enjoy the pleasures of Vienna. Like most of his confreres, he loved the student custom of spending the evenings in the coffee-houses, arguing every subject from music to medicine. From one of these discussions, one evening early that autumn, came a result of far-reaching significance to Semmelweis. One of his friends among the medical students invited him to attend the next day's anatomy demonstration. Semmelweis' curiosity made him accept readily.

The next day the young law student walked eagerly along Schwarzpanierstrasse to the gloomy building, once a rifle manufactory, which housed the ill-smelling dissecting room of Josef Berres, Professor of Anatomy. He saw the ceremonious entrance of the professor, saw the cadaver lifted dripping from its vat and placed on the dissecting table. He sickened slightly, perhaps, at the grim sight or at the pungent odor which filled the poorly ventilated room. He watched the dissector's nimble knife and listened to the accompanying lecture, only half understanding. What he did come to understand during that morning's experience, and understand thoroughly, was that his life's work was here, that medicine was the study for which his vast curiosity concerning natural science best fitted him.

The transition from student of law to student of medicine entailed little difficulty for Semmelweis. It was merely a matter of registering with the director of the medical school, which he accomplished promptly by signing the register and paying the necessary fee. His parents seem to have made no strong objection to the change.

The first year's courses in the Vienna Medical School included an introductory course in medical and surgical studies, Natural History, Systematic Anatomy, and Botany. The last, in which Semmelweis was deeply interested, was taught by the famous von Jacquin. The experience of this year convinced Semmelweis of his wisdom in altering his course of study. At its close, in the spring of 1838, he returned to Buda and stayed there for the following two academic years, continuing his medical studies at the University of Pest. He made this change perhaps for financial reasons—there were eight children in the Semmelweis family, and the burden on his father was great—perhaps because he wished to be nearer his family and friends. His professors at Pest duly shepherded him through the prescribed courses, including advanced Anatomy and Physiology, General and Animal Chemistry, Pathology and Therapeutics, but the men themselves seem to have made no lasting impression on him.

In the fall of 1840 Semmelweis returned to the Vienna Medical School. Changes were taking place in that establishment, as well as in the General Hospital. A department of Diseases of the Chest had been created, with Josef Skoda as its head. And Klein, the director of the Lying-in Hospital had changed the method of instruction in the two clinics of that institution. Formerly both medical students and midwives had been assigned in equal numbers to both clinics; now medical students alone were instructed in the First Clinic; in the Second, midwives. Within but a few months the First Clinic was to show a far higher incidence of puerperal fever than the Second. The difference became so marked that all the city gossiped of the fact, and patients begged, on admittance, to be assigned to the Second Clinic.

This occasion was, to be sure, not the first upon which the Lying-in Hospital had been a subject of public gossip. In 1822, as a result of long political persecution, the great Viennese obstetrician Lucas Boër had been ousted from his post as Director of the Lying-in Hospital on the pretext of insubordination. One of the charges asserted that he insisted in instructing students on the "phantom," or mechanical mother, refusing to use for purposes of instruction the bodies of dead mothers and their babies. This refusal was held to militate against the increasing anatomical trend of the medical school. Johann Klein, a Silesian by birth and formerly one of Boër's assistants, was recalled from his post as Professor of Obstetrics at Salzburg to take Boër's place. Klein was a rigid reactionary, firm in his loyalty to the existing regime; it is more than probable that his political influence contributed to Boër's dismissal.

Klein promptly introduced instruction from the cadaver, daily leading his students from these grim exercises straight to the wards where living women awaited their examinations. From that time on the puerperal-fever mortality in the Vienna Lying-in Hospital achieved and maintained an average many times higher than that of Boër's time. Severe epidemics occurred frequently, when even the political influence of Klein was not sufficient to stave off official investigation of his deparment. Various commissions were formed from time to time to conduct these investigations. Each in turn ineffectually paraded through the wards under Klein's guidance and arrived at the conclusion he wished it to reach: that the Professor of Obstetrics was doing all in his power to avert the pestilence, but that he was powerless, like all men, against the indefinable epidemic influence which caused it.

Semmelweis was soon deep in his studies. Two years remained, and a diversity of subjects to pursue. Obstetrics with Klein, a stern authoritarian and a tedious teacher; Ophthalmology with Rosas, a friend of Klein's and equally dogmatic; Surgery with Wattmann and Pathology and Therapeutics of Internal Diseases with von Hildenbrand, men of the same stamp. These were but half the formal course. The majority of the professors were like Klein, stalwart defenders of the *status quo*. They expected from their students unhesitating acceptance of a rigid body of dogma; criticism and questions were alike unappreciated. Although not inclined to render servile belief to statements founded only upon authority,

Semmelweis managed to perform the necessary acts of memorizing and passed through his courses creditably.

The best of his medical education came, however, from other sources, for he was not one to stop with the prescribed curriculum. He diligently visited the clinics, attended optional lectures and demonstrations, experimental and practiced dissection in the laboratories. In so doing he came under the influence of three men, all young in years, the rising stars of the Vienna Medical School, Rokitansky, Skoda, and Hebra.

Karl Freiherr von Rokitansky was a lecturer in pathological anatomy during Semmelweis' student years. Born in Bohemia in 1804, he had begun his medical studies at Prague, then transferred to Vienna. In 1834, after practicing his profession in various posts he had succeeded Wagner as Professor of Pathological Anatomy at Vienna and as Prosector to the Allgemeine Krankenhaus. His course was, however, not a required one, nor did he attain to the full professorship until 1844.

When Semmelweis first came under Rokitansky's tuition, he must have been impressed by the kindly and dependable look of the great pathologist, who was widely respected, though at best an indifferent lecturer. His habitual silence, which seemed to deprecate the need for speech, was increased during these years by his preoccupation with the preparation of a handbook of pathological anatomy, published from 1841 to 1846.

Rokitansky had much knowledge and experience to offer his students, for he was well on his way to the record of over thirty-thousand autopsies which he achieved, a record probably never surpassed by any pathologist before his day or since. Each day he worked busily in the small, poorly equipped morgue, dissecting rapidly and speaking only to dictate the results in concise, orderly phrases. The students who attended his demonstrations, Semmelweis among them, learned a whole new science of disease as shown by its consequences, learned how to trace with the dissecting knife the progress of disease through the body. And if they found their instructor habitually dry and terse, they were all the more aroused when, on the discovery of some uncommon pathological condition, Rokitansky's manner became excited and enthusiastic.

What Semmelweis learned in Rokitansky's laboratory was of inestimable value in the light of the young student's future career. For it was upon a point of pathology that Semmelweis' great discovery was to hinge—the identity of the findings in autopsies of puerperal fever cases with those in a case of "blood poisoning." It seems evident, too, that under Rokitansky's tuition Semmelweis developed a predilection for the investigation of gynecological problems which foreshadowed his subsequent decision to specialize in that field and the related one of obstetrics.

Josef Skoda, in his late thirties at this time, was a clinician, and from him Semmelweis learned the mysteries of physical diagnosis, the search for evidence of disease in the body during the early stages when treatment could still be effective. Not that Skoda or many other doctors of that period in Vienna were much concerned with the treating of disease. There was a fatalistic attitude in medicine then, for doctors were learning that many of the old theories and treatments, held inviolate for centuries, were worthless. With their foundations being gradually cut from under them, doctors were tending to become therapeutic nihilists, shrugging off all suggestions as did Skoda with the cryptic phrase, *"Ach! Das ist ja alles eins."*

Toward the methods of diagnosis Skoda showed no such apathy, but impressed their importance on his students with relentless insistence, devoting himself particularly to the new methods of percussion and auscultation. Percussion, the science of tapping the chest and other portions of the body and interpreting the resulting sounds to determine the status of the organs beneath, had been evolved by Leopold Auenbrugger in the preceding century. He learned the method of tapping wine casks to find the level of the fluid inside and applied this knowledge in ascertaining the condition of the organs of the chest, specifically the lungs. His description of his new diagnostic principle in 1761, perhaps because of its long and involved Latin title, *Inventum novum ex percussione thoracis humani ut signo abstrusos interni pectoris morbos detegendi,* roughly translated, "Detecting the signs of internal disease of the chest by percussion," had largely gone unnoticed by the medical world until translated and popularized in 1808 by Napoleon's personal physician and friend, Jean Nicholas Corvisart.

Auscultation had long been practiced by physicians, who applied the ear directly to the chest and listened to the heart and the sounds of air rushing in and out of the lungs. But such methods were far from critically accurate, although Hippocrates had described "the creaking, as of leather" to be noted in cases of pleurisy. Little progress was made in interpreting chest sounds until the development of the medical stethoscope by René Théophile Hyacinthe Laennec.

Faced with the problem of trying to hear the beating of the heart in an obese patient, Laennec remembered a trick of his childhood, in which soft taps on one end of a stick of wood could be discerned by the listener who applied his ear to the other end of the stick. A paper cylinder applied to the chest while the other end was held to his ear surprised Laennec by bringing to him the sounds of the heart "in a manner more clear and distinct than I had ever been able to do by immediate application of the ear." The stethoscope, described by Laennec in his book *Traité de l'Auscultation Mediate* (Treatise on Mediate Auscultation) in 1819, had been taken up avidly by Skoda, along with the method of percussion, to bring the science of physical diagnosis to a point of accuracy never before attained in the medical world.

A Bohemian like Rokitansky, Skoda was born in 1805, the son of a locksmith. He received his doctorate at Vienna in 1831. After two years of practice in Bohemia, he became secondary physician in the Vienna General Hospital. In this position, with a wealth of human material at his disposal, he carried on extensive research in new diagnostic methods, only to find that his faith in the powers of these methods ran counter to the established conventions of the hospital. Despite warnings, he persisted in his course, assiduously gathering material for a book. The year 1839 saw the publication of this volume, a treatise on percussion and auscultation which, at first ignored and even ridiculed, later became famous. The same year saw its obstinate author, who was accused of injuring and alarming patients by his incessant tapping and listening, removed from the General Hospital and appointed physician to the city alms-house. He soon left this post to become a police surgeon, and in 1840 when a new department of chest diseases was established at the Vienna General Hospital Skoda became its head through the influence of powerful friends in the Prague medical school and in spite of the opposition of the Vienna men, von Hildenbrand, Professor of Internal Medicine, and Schiffner, Director of the General Hospital, who had secured his demotion the year before.

Skoda's reserved, cool bearing and his carelessness of etiquette and clothes consorted well with his mental attitude in medicine, his calm rejection of authority, his firm insistence on the importance of observations and statistics. Students have described the inexorable logic with which he summed up the facts relating to difficult diagnostic problems. Beyond positive facts he refused to go; beyond the facts lay hypothesis and conjecture, in which he would take no part.

Semmelweis profited much from Skoda's teaching and it, like Rokitansky's, was to contribute greatly to his future career, for in establishing his doctrine on the etiology of puerperal fever his principal proof was such an assembly of facts and statistics as have seldom been gathered together in a medical work. He could not, however, have subscribed to Skoda's therepeutic nihilism. Semmelweis' clear head could appreciate the intellectual powers of the great clinician, but he had also a warm and sympathetic heart, which concerned itself sorely over suffering patients.

The third rising star of the Vienna Medical School was Ferdinand von Hebra, Assistant Physician in the division of Skin Diseases. Created in 1841, with Skoda—already head of the division of Chest Diseases—as its director, this department was to inaugurate the great advances in dermatology which later brought fame to the Vienna Medical School. Hebra, only twenty-five at the time of his appointment, was a brilliant and genial man, and Semmelweis, two years his junior, followed his course in dermatology with interest and profit. The two became fast friends.

These coming men, rather than the longstanding pillars of authority of the medical school, attracted and influenced Semmelweis. He voluntarily took his place at their side in the struggle they were waging against the reactionary spirits that dominated Viennese medicine. Skoda, in his vehement preaching of auscultation and percussion, had already clashed with the established powers, as has been seen, but he had powerful friends to help him. Just as von Hildenbrand and Schiffner had opposed Skoda's innovations, so were Klein, Rosas, and the other reactionaries to oppose Semmelweis' doctrine. But the story was not to end as happily.

The years passed, and at last the end of Semmelweis' medical studies came into sight. In November, 1843, he passed the first series of final examinations; in February, 1844, the second. He elected to write his dissertation in the field of botany, an indication both of his profound interest in the study of natural science and of the enthusiasm which von Jacquin and his successor von Endlicher were able to inspire in students. The title of the dissertation," De Vita Plantarum" (on the Life of Plants), indicates its nature; it was short, little more than twelve pages, a poem in prose extolling the virtues of nature.

Semmelweis read the dissertation before the faculty jury on March 2, 1844:

What spectacle can rejoice the heart of man more than the life of plants. Than those glorious flowers with their marvelous variety, exhaling their sweetest soft odors! Which furnish to our taste the most delicious of sweetness, which nourish our body and heal it of its maladies. The spirit of plants has inspired the cohort of poets, sons of divine Apollo, who are astonished by their countless forms. Man's reason cannot bring itself to understand those phenomena on which it can shed no light but which natural philosophy adopts and respects. From all that lives, in fact, emanates the omnipotence of the divine.

On he read in the same vein, with here and there a sage observation upon the influences which come to bear upon plants—heat, cold, wind, rain, parasites—and the changes they produce. It was an unusual thesis, affording ample evidence of the enthusiasm which Semmelweis brought to his studies.

The next day he was informed that his thesis had been accepted. There remained only the ceremonial graduation, at which he would receive his degree and become an accredited graduate of the leading medical school of the world.

Just before the day of graduation, Semmelweis was called to Buda by news that his mother was seriously ill. With his usual impetuousness he rushed away, without even notifying the university authorities of the reason for his abrupt departure. The lack of courtesy he displayed on this and other such occasions was to weigh against Semmelweis in later years and incur the displeasure of many. For a graduation ceremony in the Medical School of the University of Vienna was an important event, a rite of impressive solemnity, not to be lightly dismissed.

Theresa Müller Semmelweis died a few days later, from an advanced case of nephritis. A week afterwards her son returned to Vienna and on the twenty-first of April he received his medical degree.

Chapter 3

The Choice of Course

IN THE promotion book of the University of Vienna, under the date on which his medical degree was granted, appears Semmelweis' signature, appended to a declaration that he did not intend to remain in Vienna. Perhaps his hasty visit to Buda had motivated this decision; homesickness, or the desire to encourage and assist his lonely father, may have been the compelling factor. He appears to have considered a career as a general practitioner, for which his degree qualified him. But the decision was not to be followed; Hebra, Rokitansky, and Skoda may have been influential in persuading their promising student that his future lay in some special field of investigation and that he must stay in Vienna to prepare for that field.

If the three men made direct efforts to draw Semmelweis into their specialties they were doomed to disappointment. In spite of the uncongenial Profesor of Obstetrics, Klein, Semmelweis had for some time been particularly interested in obstetrics and gynecology. He now decided to specialize in these subjects. For three months in the summer of 1844 he studied hard in obstetrics, taking for the second time the two-month course in practical mid-wifery given by Johann Chiari, Klein's son-in-law and his Assistant in the Obstetrics Clinic. Chiari was but a year older than Semmelweis and the two became close friends.

One day Semmelweis watched Chiari remove a tumor from the cervix of a woman, deftly enucleating it from the neck of the uterus, from which it projected. It was a minor operation; he had seen it successfully performed several times. But childbed fever was raging then in the clinic, and a few days later this patient was dead of the disease, although she had not given birth to a child.

Chiari's explanation, based on the currently accepted theory of the etiology of puerperal fever, was that at times the "influence" which was thought to cause the fever became so strong that it attacked women who had not recently borne a child; the account probably satisfied neither him nor Semmelweis. Both knew all the accepted theories concerning the

25

dread disease which had already made the students' clinic of the Lying-in Hospital a fearful place to the women of Vienna. And both knew that none of those theories explained the strange fact that in the Second Clinic, where the midwives were trained, the fever occurred infrequently.

There were many problems in midwifery that needed the attention of a questing mind. Why did the breasts of nursing mothers become inflamed? Why did new born babies get the little pustules on their bodies that some called "impetigo"? Hebra insisted that these were only areas of infection and inflammation. Why did some babies contract the dreaded infant diarrhoea which swept the nurseries like an avenging angel? Why were babies born sometimes facing forward, sometimes backward, sometimes transversely, and at times feet first? When should the new forceps be used?

Above all, what was the nature of the great plague of lying-in mothers, the childbed fever, that came without warning, leaving bodies stacked in the post-mortem room every morning? And, most perplexing of all, how could childbed fever attack a woman who had not experienced the childbed?

On the first of August, 1844, Semmelweis passed his examinations for the degree of Master of Midwifery. A month previously he had applied to Proessor Klein for the post of Assistant in the First Obstetric Clinic. Klein, who had known Semmelweis only as an industrious and able student, received the application favorably and, after the examinations, accepted him as an aspirant for the position of Assistant, to be appointed to the post in two years when the term of the holder of the position, Dr. Breit, would run out.

The acceptance as aspirant carried with it permission to visit the Obstetric Clinic daily, and Semmelweis made the fullest use possible of this opportunity. For the following two years he spent the largest part of each day in the clinic, sometimes simply observing, sometimes actively examining patients and performing operations. Little time was left him for work in the gynecological section of the hospital, and he therefore made an arrangement with Rokitansky by which he was permitted to dissect in the pathology laboratory all corpses from the gynecological wards except those reserved for the formal pathology demonstrations. This work he did early each morning, going afterwards directly to the clinic. In later years he was to suffer great sadness at the memory of this mistaken industriousness, through which he had undoubtedly carried infection and death to many healthy women.

The year 1845 passed with Semmelweis thus occupied. He found time to study surgery and, on the thirtieth of November, took his doctorate in that field. As it was practiced in Vienna at that time, however, surgery had no charms for him. Daily he saw patients come to operation and daily he saw them carted off to the pathology laboratory. He could not find himself in a science that appeared to have as its watchwords, "Diagnosis, death, dissection."

For a time at the end of this year Semmelweis appears to have been shaken in his resolution to devote his life to obstetrics. The wavering may have resulted from disgust at the ignorance and superficiality of Klein, or from despair at the baffling problem presented by puerperal fever, which so often thwarted his skilful and energetic work in the clinic, bringing death to mothers who had seemed in perfect health.

Whatever the cause for the move, late in 1845 Semmelweis applied for the post of Assistant to Skoda, who had been appointed successor to Lippich in the professorship of Internal Medicine, to begin in 1846. Skoda had shown much interest in Semmelweis, but for some reason he did not give him the desired appointment; it went instead to a Dr. Löbel, who had assisted Skoda in the Department of Chest Diseases.

Disappointed in his attempt to change his field, Semmelweis returned as diligently as ever to the study of obstetrics. However great his disgust with the stupidities of Klein, these were pleasant months for him. He had lodgings in the Alser suburb together with a colleague from Pest, Ludwig von Markusovszky, his lifelong friend. His work was engrossing and enjoyable, despite interludes of despair. The death of his father at this time brought him great sorrow, but he found consolation in work and in friendships, few but close. Now in his twenty-eighth year, he was a vigorous and healthy young man, florid of complexion, prematurely bald, somewhat stout in build. His manner was frank and cheerful, though quiet; his speech simple, almost juvenile.

On the twenty-seventh of February 1846, Semmelweis was appointed provisional Assistant in the First Clinic, and on the first of the following July, with the end of Breit's tenure, he became Assistant. It was now his duty to examine every patient in the clinic daily in order to give the director a report on each during the latter's morning progress through the clinic. For the purpose of clinical instruction to students he had to examine all patients in labor each afternoon. In addition to these functions he was expected to be available at all times to undertake necessary operations. In spite of these arduous duties he continued his dissecting, arising even earlier than before in order to work in the pathology laboratory before going to the clinic.

Well liked by the patients, Semmelweis went about his duties cheerfully, smiling and always ready with a kind word to ease the travail of birth. There was little else that he could do, although only six months later Morton was to demonstrate the pain-relieving properties of ether at the Massachusetts General Hospital in Boston, and a year thereafter, Sir James Y. Simpson was to popularize the use of chloroform as an anesthetic in obstetrics in England.

So busy was Semmelweis that summer that he had little time even to sleep in the tiny, cell-like room he inherited from his predecessor, Breit. It was conveniently close to his duties, so close in fact that he could hear the cries of the women in labor, and, when the fever finally struck, the delirium of the dying. The percentage of deaths from puerperal fever ran high, rising from 13.10% in July, the first month of his Assistantship, to 18.05% in August.

With the beginning of his teaching duties his days and nights grew even busier. Some forty students were assigned to the First Clinic for instruction. Several were required to be in the clinic each day; called "journalists" during their tour of duty, they attended all women in labor, examining them from time to time to determine the position of the baby and the progress of labor. In the terminal stages of labor the journalists ordinarily performed all normal and some instrumental deliveries, under the supervision of the head midwife and the Assistant.

Prominent among Semmelweis' duties was the teaching of the students. His naturally retiring disposition was not as well suited to teaching as were the sarcastic sang-froid of Skoda and the gay witticisms of Ferdinand von Hebra, whom all the students loved. And his German was clumsy and heavy, disfigured by dialect.

But if Semmelweis was weak in the manner of his presentation, he was strong in the thorough knowledge of his subject. The two years spent as aspirant, in preparation for the greater responsibilities of the Assistant, had not been wasted, for he possessed an exhaustive knowledge of obstetrics. His students were inevitably impressed, too, by his zeal for the science and his careful analysis of its varied problems. And the problem which called forth his most fervent phrases was the ever-recurring one of puerperal fever, which every day undid his most careful work.

Chapter 4

The Old Hypotheses

THE THEORIES then current about puerperal fever could have been of little help to any serious student of the disease and it is not surprising that the alert mind of Semmelweis was not satisfied with them. In general, all theories of its origin postulated two influences or factors, one internal, depending upon the peculiar conditions attending pregnancy, the other external, usually dependent upon the weather or the state of the atmosphere. Various observers placed emphasis more or less upon one of these factors, but all took both into their calculations.

Among those giving prominence to internal factors, the most popular belief was that puerperal fever was due to lochial suppression. *Lochia* is the term given to the discharge from the uterus for the first week or two following delivery. In puerperal fever, the lochia is usually scanty, because, we know now, of the inflammation, but students of the disease in the eighteenth and ninteenth centuries generally reversed the concept, laying the disease to the scant discharges.

Another favorite theory was that in the freshly delivered mother, the milk accumulated inside the body, instead of being discharged through the breasts, and that its presence caused the symptoms of puerperal fever. Actually some of the writings on this theory describe "milk-pneumonia," "milk-peritonitis," and "milk-meningitis." What they were seeing, of course, was the pus from the septicemia of puerperal fever, but again they were inclined to place the cart before the horse.

The milk-fever concept was widely accepted in England and was brought to the Vienna school by Boër. Klein had learned it as Boër's assistant and since he was not one to originate new concepts, he probably passed the milk-fever theory along to his students, including Semmelweis.

Equally fallacious was the concept, widely held, that puerperal fever was caused by a vague "gastric-bilious" condition, a label placed upon many febrile illnesses of the time. Another group of obstetricians suggested as possible causative factors the emotions—fear, shame, and the like. Still another group felt that a peculiar set of conditions in the lying-in woman, a congestion or loading of the blood and tissues, kept her constantly on the verge of a fever, ready to succumb whenever any of several external factors was present. And as an even wilder example of setting the cart before the horse, some doctors, noting the fibrin deposits on the abdominal organs from the inflammation characteristic of the disease, postulated an increase in fibrin in the mother's blood, leading to a "crasis" or "blood dissolution."

The explanations of the disease based upon outside influences were, as has been said, variously combined with those theories concerning internal factors. The atmosphere itself was suspect, and the specific atmosphere of lying-in hospitals came under suspicion as well, with more reason. Doctors spoke darkly of other "influences," whose nature was vague in the extreme. Some were described as "cosmic" or "telluric" influences, or as "miasmas," atmosphere-borne states which were thought to cause many diseases. A logical extension of this belief was the "contagion theory," consisting in the belief that when the disease appeared in a patient, it shortly brought into existence a specific emanation, labeled a virus (but not in the sense of the modern ultra-microscopic organism), which spread by various means to infect others with the fever. This belief was popular in England, while continental obstetricians leaned to the theory of air-borne epidemic influences. Thus Semmelweis was probably taught to be a "milk-fever epidemicist."

An occasional obstetrician, even in those days, recognized puerperal fever as what it is, a wound infection, but even so, none knew what the noxious agent was, how it reached the vulnerable area, or how it could be destroyed or excluded. For the most part the obstetricians of the continent, with their belief in an epidemic influence which they were powerless to fight, threw up their hands. In England, on the other hand, the concept of a *contagium*, however nebulous it was, led to vigorous antiseptic measures which produced rather remarkable results.

John Burton in England was the first author to suggest, in 1751, that puerperal fever was brought to the patient by an outstanding agency, intimating that the carelessness of the midwife or the attendants might be the cause. Others made similar observations but gave no specific contribution, until Dr. Charles White of Manchester, England, pointed out clearly the most significant facts in preventing the spread of the disease. Even White, for all that he was far ahead of any-one else in the search for truth, had no real concept of the exact method of infection by which the recently delivered mother developed puerperal fever; he leaned toward the con-cept of stagnation of the lochia, made putrid by the access of air following delivery.

Charles White's book, *A Treatise on the Management of Pregnant and Lying-in Women, and the Means of Curing, More Especially of Preventing, the Principal Disorders to Which They Are Liable,* was published in Manchester in 1773 and went into five editions in twenty years. It was translated into many languages, including the German, so it is not im-probable that Semmelweis was himself familiar with it. An American edition appeared in 1793. White's description of obstetric practice in the latter half of the eighteenth century is very illuminating. He describes how the woman in labor was confined in a small, unventilated room, filled with her friends. A large fire brought the temperature to an unendur-able height, but the attendants produced further discomfort in the patient by "pouring into her" numerous warm alcoholic drinks, to diminish her pains if too strong, to increase them if too weak. The delivery over, she was covered with additional blankets, the bed curtains were pinned close around her, and every crevice that might let in fresh air was effectually sealed. The diet of warm liquors was continued to the exclusion of other food.

Among the poor, living in cellars, White observed even worse conditions, aggravated by "the dampness and closeness of their houses, and the want of clean linen, and cleanliness in general." Garrets were no better, for there the patients were subjected to the "putrid miasmata" of the families living below.

Charles White protected his patients with a strict regimen of cleanliness, fresh air, and hygiene, allowing them to sit up a few hours after delivery and insisting that they get out of bed on the same day, if possible. This recommendation, start-ling for that day, is interesting in view of the widely spreading modern obstetric practice of getting patients up very soon after delivery. His success was remarkable for that or any day, for in later years he stated that in a long obstetric practice he had not lost a single patient from puerperal fever.

Once the disease had developed, White's treatment was surprisingly modern. He had the patient placed in a semi-recumbent position and ordered mild antiseptic douches. He stipulated that, if a separate room could not be given to each patient at the outset, any patient who took the fever should immediately be moved into a separate room, for the safety of the other patients as much as for her own. As soon as the fever patient had recovered, the room in which she was confined was thoroughly cleansed, the bedding and curtains washed, the floor and woodwork wiped with vinegar. The healthfulness of the room would be increased, he added, "if it were stoved with brimstone."

One of the first physicians to give a clear-cut statement on the contagious nature of childbed fever, was Alexander Gordon of Aberdeen, in 1795. In his *Treatise on the Epidemic Puerperal Fever* (London, 1795), Gordon stated:

That the cause of the disease was a specific contagion or infection, I have unquestionable proof. This disease seized such women only, as were visited, or delivered, by a practitioner, or taken care of by a nurse, who had previously attended patients affected with the disease. Every person, who had been with a patient in the Puerperal Fever, became charged with an atmosphere of infection, which was communicated to every pregnant woman, who happened to come within its sphere.

Gordon further recommended burning of the bedclothes and apparel of infected patients and advised thorough washing of the person of the attendant doctors and nurses, together with fumigation of their apparel. His theory of the disease was remarkable, also, in that he labeled it as an erysipelas, thus closely approaching our modern knowledge that both erysipelas of the skin and puerperal fever are caused by streptococci. Nevertheless, it is apparent that, subscribing to the theory of the *contagium,* Gordon did not understand the true nature of the agent which was transmitted from the infected to the uninfected woman.

The account by Robert Collins, as master of the famous Rotunda Hospital in Dublin, long one of the great centers of obstetrical knowledge, gives an excellent picture of the practice of the most enlightened among the English "contagionists" prior to Semmelweis. When Collins entered into the position of Master of the Rotunda (a position similar to the Assistantship held by Semmelweis at the Allgemeine Krankenhaus of Vienna) puerperal fever was raging in the hospital. Decreasing in 1827, it broke out again in 1828 and became so severe in February 1829, that Collins had all the rooms of the Rotunda filled in turn with nascent chlorine gas for forty-eight hours, with all openings sealed. The walls and floors were also treated with chloride of lime in the form of a paste. After the woodwork had been painted, the walls and ceilings were washed down with fresh lime. Blankets and similar articles of bedding were secured and then treated with dry heat in a stove at 120° to 130° Fahrenheit. By such measures, Collins was able to control the epidemic and reduce the mortality from childbirth in 10,785 deliveries to 0.53%, without a single case of childbed fever.

Still another pungent observation on the malady of the childbed was made in 1834 by James Blundell of London:

That the fever may occur spontaneously, I admit; that its infectious character may be plausibly disputed, I do not deny; but I add, considerately, that in my own family, I had rather that those I esteemed the most be delivered, unaided, in a stable, by the manger-side, than that they should receive the best help, in the fairest apartment, but exposed to the vapors of this pitiless disease. Gossiping friends, wet nurses, monthly nurses, the practitioner himself, these are the chambers by which the infection is principally conveyed.

In America another voice had been lifted against the unnecessary toll taken of lying-in mothers by puerperal infection. Oliver Wendell Holmes, better known as a man of letters, was also an outstanding medical thinker. He was familiar with the literature on obstetrics and puerperal fever in England, and probably with much of the continental literature as well, since he was a prodigious reader. Judging from these reports, and from many cases which had been described to him by other physicians, Holmes stated his beliefs bluntly in 1843 in his famous article: "The Contagiousness of Puerperal Fever": "The disease known as Puerperal Fever is so far contagious as to be frequently carried from patient to patient by physicians and nurses."

Holmes arrayed a formidable list of instances in which puerperal fever had followed treatment by physicians who, before going to the delivery had performed post-morten examinations upon cases of gangrene, erysipelas, peritonitis, and other such inflammatory conditions, or treated other cases of puerperal infection and the like.

Of the performance of post-mortems in particular he said:

It seems proper to allude to the dangerous and often fatal effects which have followed wounds received in the post-mortem examination of patients who have died of puerperal fever. . . . Now a moment's reflection will show that the number of cases of serious consequence ensuing from the dissection of the bodies of those who have perished from puerperal fever, is so vastly disproportioned to the relatively small number of autopsies made in this complaint as compared with typhus, or pneumonia, and still more from all diseases put together, that the conclusion is irresistible that a most fearful morbid poison is often generated in the course of this disease. Whether or not it is *sui generis,* confined to this disease, or produced in some others, as for instance erysipelas, I need not stop to inquire.

Now add to this the undisputed fact that within the walls of the lying-in hospitals there is generated a miasma, palpable as the chlorine used to destroy it [a reference to the work of Collins at the Rotunda], tenacious so as in some cases almost to defy extirpation, deadly in some institutions as the plague; which has killed in a private hospital of London so fast that they were buried two in one coffin to conceal its horrors; which enabled Tonelle to record two hundred and twenty-two autopsies at the Maternité of Paris; which has led Dr. Lee to express his deliberate conviction that the loss of life occasioned by these institutions completely defeats the object of their founders; and out of this train of cumulative evidence, the multiplied groups of cases clustering about the individuals, the deadly results of autopsies, the inoculation by fluids from the living patient, the murderous poison of hospitals, does there not result a conclusion that laughs all sophistry to scorn and renders all arguments an insult?

The very positiveness of Holmes' opinions, as well as his radical departure from the then accepted pattern of thinking earned for him an immediate storm of abuse from professors of obstetrics all over America, and chiefly from the very practitioners who most needed his advice. Like many another prophet he was not accepted in his own country and his suggestions were practiced by very few of the obstetricians of his day. Yet he came very close indeed to the truth. Only in failing, as did the others, to recognize the way in which the infection was carried to lying-in mothers from all these sources did he fall behind the great discovery of Semmelweis.

All these pronouncements, important though they were, had not prepared medical men to admit that they were themselves the guilty agents in puerperal-fever epidemics. Holmes' eloquence evoked bitter controversy in America, and in Britain the traditions of White, Gordon, and Collins were not very widely accepted. In Europe the same old unclean practices persisted and epidemics of puerperal fever were as numerous and as violent as ever. The world was not yet ready to be converted, as Semmelweis was to learn when, four years after Holmes' article, he began to practice antisepsis in the obstetric clinic of Vienna's great hospital.

Chapter 5

The Problem Faced

FROM THE PATHOLOGICAL LABORATORY where they made early-morning dissections upon cadavers, many students in the Vienna Medical School went directly to the lying-in wards. There they congregated in one of the small rooms waiting for the coming of the Professor or the Assistant, Semmelweis in this case, to begin the teaching. The ones who had been dissecting washed their hands perfunctorily under the tap and dried them on dirty handkerchiefs or waved them in the air.

The students brought with them from the pathological laboratory, in their stained overalls and on their hands, the dank nauseating odor which clung to them from the moment they began their dissections until they had finished the course. The same odor permeated Semmelweis' own clothes, for he continued to work steadily, early every morning, in the pathology laboratory. Often his friend Hebra worked there with him, having chosen to enter a field with which few doctors troubled themselves, the vexing problems of skin diseases. He studied the manifestations of disease in the skin of patients in the clinic, at the autopsy table, and under the microscope. His methods were bringing notable results, too, and the classification he was developing was to be recognized shortly as the greatest contribution to dermatology up to that time.

Even more successful as a teacher than as a diagnostician,

Hebra possessed a brilliant personality, ebullient, gay, and charming. Although he was the youngest of the greater teachers of the Vienna Medical School, his clinics drew many students.

Hebra was very active politically and was often disgusted when he could arouse no enthusiasm comparable with his own in his Hungarian friend. Semmelweis was, of course, aware of the unrest that stirred Hungary and practically every country in Europe in those years following the successful and bloody Revolution in France. And he would not have been the patriotic Hungarian that he was if he had not secretly sympathized with the preachings of Kossuth, the fiery Hungarian radical whose downfall was to plunge his country into a misery greater than she had ever known.

In common with many of the younger men of Vienna, Hebra argued that Austria, too, should rise and throw off the yoke of the tyrant, as had France and America, and as was advocated by Kossuth for Hungary. Some even went so far as to shout in moments of excitement, in the coffeehouses and the quarters of the students and younger members of the faculty, that Austria should form a republic and free herself from the rule of the Hapsburgs.

There was danger in that sort of talk, as they all well knew, but it only lent excitement. Metternich, it was commonly known, had spies everywhere, so intricate was the net he had woven over Central Europe, and one who was indiscreet might find himself suddenly occupying a dungeon instead of a chair at the University.

A definite schism existed in the ranks of the students and teachers. The older group, more cautious, were all for consevatism and urged the massing of all the powers of royalism in Europe against such subversive movements as that which had bathed France in blood. The younger group, among them Hebra and a somewhat lukewarm Semmelweis, were all for change, by revolution if necessary, to get rid of the despotic rule of the Hapsburgs and to accomplish the downfall of Metternich and the policy of "stability," under which he sought to erase every spark of independence in the Empire.

Semmelweis had little time or inclination, in the fall of 1846, for the fruitless shoutings and arm-wavings of the would-be revolutionaries. There was trouble in the Krankenhaus, in the First Division of the Lying-in Hospital, where it seemed there was always trouble. Childbed fever raged. From

May to July, the mortality had averaged 12.23%; in August it rose to 18.05%, in September and October it stood about 14%. In general, the rate was four times as great as that of the Second Clinic. Why this amazing difference when the two departments were actually part of the same building?

Diligently he searched the literature for some clue as to the dread infection. Almost every hospital in Europe had it; some were worse—the Paris Maternité, for example, was far worse than Vienna. Every conceivable theory as to etiology had been suggested—every theory but the right one. Semmelweis must have studied the English theories of contagion, for he refers to them later in his own writings, but the elusive something—the *contagium*—to which the English attributed the disease was much too evanescent to satisfy the logical mind of the young obstetrician.

One after another he subjected the current theories in regard to puerperal fever to the cold logic of his knowledge and experience, the critical analysis of his penetrating mind. He weighed each theory against the one undeniable truth in his possession, the difference between the puerperal-fever mortality in the First and Second Clinics; balanced against that truth each theory was found wanting.

Semmelweis' unceasing search for a theory that would bear this test is described for us in his own words in the book which he published years later on the etiology, nature, and prevention of puerperal fever. From *Die Ætiologie* the biographer of Semmelweis is impelled to quote freely, for nowhere else is the story told with such authority and force, and no secondary rendering could convey the sense of remorseless, unwearying, logical progression which the original gives.

To the most freely accepted theory in Vienna, that childbed fever resulted from atmospheric-cosmic-telluric conditions, which often became epidemic, i.e., occurred in very great power and numbers, Semmelweis replied:

Now, if the atmospheric-cosmic-telluric conditions of the City of Vienna are so disposed that they cause puerperal fever in individuals susceptible thereto as puerperae, how does it happen that these atmospheric-cosmic-telluric conditions over such a long period of years have carried off individuals disposed thereto as puerperae in the First Clinic, while they have so strikingly spared others also in Vienna, even in the same building in the Second Division and similarly vulnerable as puerperae? To me, there is not the slightest doubt that, if the devastation by childbed fever in the First Clinic must be attributed to epidemic influences, then these same influences must be effective also in the Second Clinic with very small variations, otherwise one will be forced to the absurd assumption that the epidemic influences must be subject to twenty-four hour remissions and exacerbations in their pernicious activity, and that the remissions through successive years just coincide with the admission days for the Second Clinic, while the exacerbations over a number of years set in exactly at the time admissions are made to the First Division. But even then, if one might accept so manifest an aburdity, the difference in mortality between the two divisions under epidemic influences will not be explained. The epidemic influences are working upon the individual either before her admission to the lying-in hospital, or they work upon her during her stay. If they affect the individual outside the maternity hospital, then those admitted to the First Division are certain, as well as those who present themselves at the Second Division for admission, to be exposed to the pernicious action of the epidemic influences outside the lying-in hospital, and then such a great difference in the mortality ratios could not exist in the two divisions, both of which admit individuals subject to epidemic influences. But if the epidemic influences affect an individual during her sojourn in the maternity hospital, then again there could be no difference in the mortality ratios, because the two divisions, which are so close to each other that they have a common anteroom, must necessarily be subject to the same atmospheric-cosmic-telluric influences. These were the considerations which forced upon me the unshakeable conviction that it was not the epidemic influences which wrought the frightful havoc among the puerperae of the First Obstetrical Clinic.

After this unshakeable anti-epidemic conviction had once taken possession of me, many reasons soon presented themselves which made me more and more firm in my conviction. We shall take them up as follows:

If the atmospheric influences in the City of Vienna provoked the epidemic of childbed fever, the childbed fever—since the population of the City of Vienna was exposed to the same influences—should of necessity prevail among the puerperae in the city, but actually during the greatest height of the puerperal disease in the lying-in hospital there was not observed, either in Vienna or in the rural districts, any increased morbidity [sickness] among the puerperae. . . .

A very frequent and certainly a successful measure for arresting the progress of an epidemic of childbed fever is to close the lying-in hospital. The lying-in hospital is not closed with the intention that the puerperae should die outside of the hospital, but with the conviction that if they deliver in the lying-in hospital they will succumb to the epidemic influences, and if they are confined outside, they will remain healthy. Thus it is proven that there is no epidemic to deal with: i.e., a disease which depends upon atmospheric influences, because the atmospheric influences reach beyond the walls of the lying-in hospital and extend to the parturients and puerperae in any corner whatsoever of the city; thus it is shown that these are endemics, i.e., a disease which is the result of causes confined within the walls of the lying-in hospital. . . .

Puerperal fever, which is the result of a traumatic cause, e.g., a difficult forceps delivery, is during its course and in its anatomic findings the same as it is in the so-called epidemic form. Can indeed any other epidemic disease be engendered by traumatic means?

Epidemics have periodic intermissions, but childbed fever has raged continuously for a long period of years in the First Obstetrical Clinic with but trifling interruptions. . . .

If the so-called epidemic of childbed fever were actually dependent upon atmospheric influences, it could not then occur during the different seasons of the year and in the various climates; as a matter of fact, epidemics of childbed fever have been observed at all seasons of the year, in different climates and under all sorts of atmospheric conditions.

Semmelweis constructed a table covering several years' experience in the Vienna Hospital in which he showed that the mortality from childbed fever varied widely during any single month from year to year. The conclusion which he drew from this circumstance gave further weight to his argument against epidemic influences:

The reader will observe, that the epidemic influences are so powerful that their pernicious activity cannot be restrained at any season of the year, that they rage in the depth of winter and during the oppressive summer heat with equal violence; however, the epidemic influences are partial in that they do not scourge all lying-in hospitals to the same extent, but spare certain institutions and decimate the inmates of others without mercy. Indeed they go so far in their partiality, as even to attack with unequal severity different sections of one and the same institution. . . .

These findings have strengthened more and more my conviction that the enormous mortality in the First Obstetrical Clinic is not caused by epidemic influences, but that there are endemic noxious agents which manifest themselves in such a frightful fashion only within the limits of the First Obstetrical Clinic.

Surely no logic could be simpler than this, yet the vague theory of cosmic-telluric influences, which at times attained epidemic character, was accepted widely throughout the Continent, as well as in Vienna, and continued to be preached by many obstetricians for twenty-five years.

There were other theories, equally absurd, but shared by many influential men, upon which Semmelweis directed the merciless light of logic, always stressing the obvious, and yet to him totally inexplicable, fact that so many more women died in the First Clinic than in the Second, although the circumstances were so nearly the same in both.

Of overcrowding, often stressed as a cause, he said:

If overcrowding were the cause of the fatalities in the First Obstetrical Clinic, then the mortality in the Second Obstetrical Clinic should have been still greater because the Second Obstetrical Clinic was even more overcrowded than the first. The bad repute of the First Obstetrical Clinic was such that everyone strove for admission into the Second Clinic, and thus it often happened that the Second Division, although the appointed time drew near, could not take over the admissions because there was no room for the new arrivals, or even if new admissions were taken in, then, after the passage of only a few hours until the appointed time was up, they must be returned to the First Division, because such an enormous crowd of people in the corridors awaited the time for the shift of admissions from the First Clinic to the Second [every twenty-four hours], that, during the course of a rather short time, all the available places were occupied. During the . . . years which I spent in the First Clinic, it was never once necessary, on account of overcrowding, to turn the admissions over to the Second Clinic before the appointed time, even though at the First Clinic the admissions continued for 48 hours without a break [on Saturdays and Sundays]; and in spite of this overcrowding, the mortality in the Second Clinic was strikingly less.

What harrowing scenes must have occurred when people jammed the corridors, waiting for the regular daily change from admission to the First Clinic, with its dread reputation, to the Second. In answer to the assertion that the fear of women in the First Clinic was a possible source of the puerperal fever Semmelweis said:

It is believed that the ill repute of the institution causes the newly admitted patients to enter the building only in terror, because it is well known to them how large a contingent the institution gives over to death each year and that this belief causes them to sicken and die. That they really dread the First Division can readily be demonstrated, because one must endure heart-rending scenes, when women, wringing their hands, beg on bended knee for their release, in order to seek admission to the Second Divi-

sion after having hit upon the First Division because of un-
familiarity with the place, which the presence of many men
[students] made clear to them. Puerperae with uncountable
pulse-rates, enormously distended abdomens, dry tongues, i.e.,
gravely ill with puerperal fever, assured me a few hours before
death, that they were entirely well, in order to escape treatment by
the physicians, because they realized that such treatment was the
forerunner of Death. In spite of this, I could not convince myself
that fear was the cause of the greater mortality in the First Division, because I as a physician could not understand how terror,
a psychic state, could produce such material changes as are found
in childbed fever. Besides this, a longer period must have gone by
and a greater mortality must necessarily have taken place, before
it became known among the people, to whom the lying-in hospital statistics are not accessible, that more persons die in one
division than in another. The origin of the mortality is not to be
explained by fear.

Thus, one by one, the theories were discarded and in the
end he was forced to conclude: "I could not discover in the
hitherto prevailing principles underlying the etiology of puerperal fever the actual existence of the alleged etiological factors in the many hundreds of cases which I saw treated in
vain."

Convinced that the answer to the problem of childbed fever
did not lie in the accepted theories, and that something inside
the Lying-in Hospital, possibly something inside the First
Clinic itself, was the cause, Semmelweis turned his logic upon
that unfortunate division.

Chapter 6

The Search for Clues

WHEN HE BEGAN to search inside the First Clinic of the
Lying-in Hospital for the answer to this problem in death,
Semmelweis at first found little more than he had in studying
external influences. In desperation he grasped at anything
which seemed to offer hope. He tells in *Die Ætiologie* how he
came to suspect that the religious practices in the obstetrical
clinic might be responsible for the greater mortality of the
First Clinic.

The priest coming from the chapel of the General Hospital

to administer the last rites to the dying could reach the sick-wards of the Second Clinic without passing through the other rooms. In the First Clinic, however, he had to pass through five rooms to reach the sick-wards. It was customary for the priest to come attired in his vestments, a sacristan preceding him and ringing a bell. It was often necessary for the priest to come several times in the day and the night as well, for women who seemed well at the time of his regular visit and therefore did not receive the sacrament sometimes declined within a few hours so that he had to be summoned again. The lying-in women in the outer wards of the First Clinic needed no explanation of his repeated visits, and it was inevitable that "the ominous sound of the little bell" should put the fear of death into their hearts.

Neglecting no possibilities, Semmelweis determined to eliminate this cause of stress, to which the women of the First Clinic and not those of the Second were subjected:

During my first term of service, I appealed to the humanity of this servant of God and without difficulty attained my wish that the priest in the future should go in a roundabout way to the wards, unattended and without the ringing of the bell and without passing through the other wards, so no one was aware of the presence of the priest, outside of the patients actually in the ward.

The bell of the sacristan was no longer heard in the wards of the First Division, and the candlelight no longer flickered in the fear-dulled eyes of the women in the long rows of beds, well today, who might be at the end of life's path tomorrow. And no more did the sound of the bell crash upon the tense and weary figure humped over books and journals in the small room belonging to the Assistant. But the women continued to die and soon it was again obvious that the fear of death was not the cause of puerperal fever.

Through constant practice during his period as aspirant, Semmelweis had become highly skilled in obstetrical operations. Each group of journalists, as medical students have always done, vied with each other to be present at a delivery by the still novel method of the forceps.

Perhaps in his enthusiasm for the forceps, Semmelweis did use them more than was absolutely necessary, certainly more than had Professor Boër, Klein's predecessor as director of the Lying-in Hospital. Sent by Emperor Joseph II to France and England to study midwifery, Boër had brought back from the latter country a theory of the "natural way" in midwifery and had followed his conservative methods with marked success throughout thirty-four years of service. To some extent these methods continued to prevail under Klein's regime, but operations became far more numerous. In later year Semmelweis was to refer to his own frequent use of forceps as probably having contributed to the death of many women from childbed fever. Often he would be aroused by the head midwife in the middle of the night because one of the patients was not progressing satisfactorily. A quick examination usually showed the failure of the child's head to rotate into position with the back of the head just under the mother's pubic bone, the most frequent complication in first mothers. Then out would come the forceps from their case in the corner of the room.

They were handsome instruments, with their slender handles and double curved blades. One curve enabled them to be inserted into the birth canal; the flat blades were then curved again so that they fitted snugly on either side of the child's head between the skull and the rigid walls of the mother's pelvis. Elliptical rings at the end of each blade enclosed the ears of the child when the blades were locked into position. Thus, without compressing the child's head, the obstetrician could exert a downward pull upon the body and rotate the head into a position better calculated to permit its passage from the mother's body into the world.

With these efficient tools delivery was usually quick and sure, though there was nothing, in those days before anesthesia, to dull the agony of the mother as the unyielding metal of the blades pressed against the bruised tissues of her body. All too frequently, however, the success of the operation was tempered by the sober realization that these cases very often developed childbed fever, and that in a few days the young mother would be raving in delirium, or lying comatose in the last stages of the dread infection.

Yet Semmelweis could not bring himself to believe that the cause of puerperal fever lay in the obstetrical treatment itself, the many and rough operations in the First Clinic, as some alleged. Boër's principles were still followed in both divisions, and the major proportion of the mothers had no obstetrical operations at all.

Nor could Semmelweis believe that the therapeutic measures taken in cases of puerperal fever contributed in any way to the greater mortality of the disease in the First Clinic. He knew that these cases received identical treatment in both divisions of the Lying-in Hospital. If the treatment alone were at fault the two clinics should show the same mortality. But the trouble was not that more women died from the disease in the First Clinic, but that more women contracted the disease there. If further evidence were needed, there was the fact that when all sick mothers were transferred to the General Hospital, as was frequently the case in severe epidemics, they died just as frequently under different medical treatment.

Continually he searched for clues to the mystery of the dying mothers and continually the one he was looking for eluded him. Could there be any possible effect upon the mothers from walking to their beds some three or four hours after delivery? That question was settled by the fact that women from both divisions walked to their beds and, in truth, those in the Second Division had to pass through an unheated anteroom. What of the ventilation? As bad as it was, there was no difference in the two clinics. Could the fact that linen from the Lying-in Hospital was mixed with that from the General Hospital be of importance? Hardly, he observed, when the Second Division used similar linen.

Again and again Semmelweis considered suggested causes for the amazing difference in death rates between the two clinics. And again and again he was forced to reject them, after devoting to each question the thoroughness and penetration with which he approached his study. Scientific discovery, of course, is rarely a matter of happenstance, for the true scientist approaches his problem gradually, weighing and evaluating each finding as he proceeds, discarding the valueless, and attempting to place the pertinent in its correct relationship to other factors. Rarely has the value of this method been demonstrated more effectively than in the search by Semmelweis for the cause of childbed fever, but for the moment the answer still eluded him.

Fundamentally kind and considerate, Semmelweis was troubled particularly by the high death rates among young mothers in their initial experience with childbirth. The labors of primiparae (women pregnant for the first time) are always long, since the slowly yielding tissues of the birth passage must be dilated sufficiently to allow the child's head and body to pass through. And this very length of labor seemed to make them particularly susceptible to puerperal fever:

Slow progress in the first stage occurred as a rule only in primiparae. . . . Time and time again I have pointed out to my pupils, that these blooming young girls teeming with health, because their period of dilatation was prolonged, would become ill, either during labor itself or shortly after delivery, of a rapidly progressive puerperal fever. My prognosis was realized; I did not know, to be sure, why this happened, but I saw it happen often; the fact was the more inexplicable because it was not repeated in the Second Division under similar conditions.

But Semmelweis was gradually approaching the truth, although he was probably not cognizant that he had made any progress at all. Deep inside his agile brain evidence was being weighed and sifted, evidence which would culminate one day in the blinding realization of how these mothers received the lethal infection. Meanwhile there was the perplexing problem of the street-births.

The Lying-in Hospital was a charity institution and operated also a foundling hospital, in which illegitimate children were cared for and adoption arranged or orphanage care assured. But for a mother to be eligible for treatment and her child for the privileges of the foundling hospital, she must allow herself to be used for instruction during her labor and must do duty thereafter as a wet nurse in the foundling hospital, if she were able. There was a provision, however, that those who started for the hospital but were unable to get there before the baby was born, could be admitted, provided the infant had not been washed and the stump of the umbilical cord was still fresh, these circumstances being taken as evidence that birth had indeed been precipitate. Such births were called "street-births," or *gassengeburten*.

It was common knowledge in Vienna that while many actual street-births did really occur, many girls with illegitimate pregnancies, not wanting to be used for teaching purposes, were delivered by midwives and subsequently driven to the hospital with the newborn baby, claiming to have given birth on the way to the hospital. Their number was large, for Semmelweis mentions as many as a hundred monthly in both divisions. It was not, however, their number which puzzled him, but their relative immunity from puerperal fever in spite of the dirt and filth which attended public accouchement, for he says:

I have noticed that just those women who have had street-births become ill noticeably less often than those delivered in the hospital, despite the fact that the street births obviously occur under more unfavorable circumstances than those delivered on our delivery beds. It should not be objected that the majority are delivered in bed with the assistance of a midwife, and that our puerperae must seek their beds on foot three hours after delivery, for this walk over a passageway, glass enclosed and heated in winter, is certainly less harmful than to be delivered by a midwife, there also to get up soon after labor and to go from God-knows-how-many-floors-up down to a carrige and to travel in every sort of weather over wretched pavement to the hospital and there to mount again to the first floor. To those who are actually delivered in the street this applies to a still greater degree.

It seemed logical to me, that the puerperae who have undergone a so-called street delivery should become ill at least as often, if not more frequently, than those delivered in the hospital.

But they did not. What was the answer?

Ever searching, Semmelweis tackled another aspect of the problem. On the grounds of pure deduction he proved that puerperal fever was not, as generally believed except in England, a disease peculiar to women in the pregnant state. This conclusion came as a result of his studies of newborns who died in a similar manner to their mothers:

Again, not only these mothers [with prolonged labors], but even their newborn children, whether male or female, have all died of puerperal fever. I am not the only one who speaks of puerperal fever in the newborn. The anatomical findings in the cadavers of such newborn were, with the exception of the genital organs, identical with findings in the dead bodies of puerperae who succumbed to puerperal fever. To recognize these changes in the bodies of the puerperae and not to recognize identical results in the bodies of the newborn, invalidates the pathological anatomy.

If it is one and the same disease from which the puerperae and the newborn die, then there must be the same etiology for the newborn which is admitted as applicable to the mothers. Since this same difference in mortality which we observe among the puerperae of the two clinics repeats itself among the newborn, i.e., in the First Division, the newborn also die in much larger numbers than in the Second Division, then the hitherto accepted etiology of childbed fever shows itself to be just as deficient in explaining the difference in the mortality among the newborn from childbed fever as it has been in the explanation of the difference in the mortality among the puerperae.

Semmelweis was getting somewhere, for all his disappointments, for he was now confirmed in his belief that the evil originated within the First Clinic. He had developed, in fact, an "unshakeable conviction that the mortality in the First Clinic is not contingent upon epidemic influences, but that there are endemic, as yet unknown noxious agents, i.e., harmful things, which manifest their pernicious activity within the limits of the First Clinic." And, guided by this firm belief, he set himself again to study differences between the two clinics which might offer further clues in solving the mystery of the dying mothers.

In Semmelweis' troubled mind, one fact recurred over and over again, as it does in his writings: the remarkable difference in the incidence of childbed fever between the Second Clinic where the midwives were trained, and the First, which was the domain of the students. In most ways the two divisions were exactly alike, differing only in the position which was used in delivery, the Second Clinic mothers being delivered lying on their sides in what was called the "lateral position," while in the students' Clinic the more orthodox dorsal position was used.

In desperation he ordered that henceforth all deliveries in the First Division should be in the lateral position. It was not easy to change the routine method of delivery in the First Division overnight. The students and the midwives of that section had become accustomed to the "dorsal," or back position, and they resented the change. But Semmelweis, as always, insisted that his new routine be meticulously obeyed. He directed it himself, losing much sleep in the process, for the midwives and the students were not above turning the women on their backs at the last moment, if he was not looking.

But the fever raged in the First Division unchecked. And still the young mothers came, for they had no place to go save the forbidding Krankenhaus. One day they were assigned to the Second Division, had their babies, and a week later, well and happy, departed for the hovels and the overcrowded *zinstpalaestes* they called home. The next day all the mothers were sent to the First Division, and many did not leave, save through the grim portals of Rokitansky's laboratory.

Once more a straw grasped at had proved futile, and wearily Semmelweis ordered that the normal position of delivery in the First Division should be resumed. But although foiled for the moment in the fulfillment of his burning desire to stop this toll of death, Semmelweis was making progress. As he disposed one by one of the accepted arguments used to explain childbed fever, always narrowing the field, the truth came nearer and nearer.

Satisfied that something inside the First Clinic itself was causing the deaths, he talked of his findings here and there, in the dining rooms, and in the occasional sessions over beer and cheese in the coffee-houses frequented by the students and the younger instructors. It was inevitable that some of this talk should reach the ears of Professor Klein, particularly since the spy system inside the Krankenhaus was well known to be practically as effective as that of Metternich for the nation. And in Klein's brain such theories were bound to stir anger, for they smacked of the English theory of contagion, evolved by such men as Charles White of Manchester, Gordon of Aberdeen, and Collins of the Rotunda Hospital, Dublin.

If Semmelweis had chosen to introduce the English theory of contagion into the First Division of the Lying-in Hospital (and there is no evidence to show that he did accept the contagion theory in full), he would have gotten nowhere. Klein had just published a long monograph in which he exploded, to his own satisfaction at least, the English theories.

Attacking the contagion theory was a labor of love with Klein. Professor Boër, his predecessor in the Lying-in Hospital, had put the English ideas of cleanliness into effect in 1789. Boër's record over the next twenty years of 65,000 deliveries with an average mortality of 1.3%, culminating in the achievement in his last year as professor of obstetrics of a mortality of only 0.8%, must have been a sore point with Klein. That worthy, in his first year in the position, managed to attain a death rate of 7.8%, and rarely had his record been much better since. Only his entrenched position in the medical politics which dominated the Vienna school kept him in the chair of obstetrics.

Naturally Klein was sensitive to criticism on this score, and it is reasonable to suppose that reports of criticism by his own Assistant aroused in him indignation, even fury. Nor was it impotent fury. Breit, Semmelweis' predecessor, applied for another term as Assistant. Klein, contrary to the custom of the department, granted the application, and on October 20, after less than four months of service in the position for which he had waited two years, Semmelweis was demoted to the post of aspirant.

The demotion must have been a severe blow to the young obstetrician. He had powerful friends in the hospital and in the medical school—Skoda, Rokitansky, Hebra; Kolletschka, the brilliant professor of legal medicine and jurisprudence; Haller, the chief physician; but they could give him nothing but sympathy. Klein was very close to the Minister of Education, and everyone knew that nothing could be gained by protesting the dismissal of the brilliant young obstetrician.

It can have been but small consolation to Semmelweis when, a month after his dismissal, rumors of the terrible state of affairs in the Lying-in Hospital reached the Emperor's court. An investigation was demanded and, in spite of Klein's political influence, he found it necessary to accede.

A commission was appointed, but it did not consist of scientists like Skoda, Rokitansky, or Kolletschka, or even Semmelweis, who knew far more about puerperal fever than anyone in Vienna. Instead the members were mere *höflinge,* placemen, friends of Klein and cut from the same dull pattern. Steeped in didacticism, hardly able to see beyond their academic and highly sensitive noses, the commission was a total failure. The men snooped through the Lying-in Hospital for a few hours, listened to Klein in his office for an hour, and did not even hear the evidence of the one man who might have helped them.

In the end the commissioners arrived at the naive conclusion that the existing puerperal "epidemic" was the result of injuries to the genital organs brought about by the many examinations made in the course of instruction. The investigators claimed that the greater mortality in the First Clinic was due to the fact that the male students performed these examinations more roughly than did the pupil midwives of the Second Clinic. They fixed particular blame on the foreign students, accusing them of being rougher in examining than were the Austrian students.

As a result the number of students instructed in the First Clinic was reduced from forty-two to twenty, foreigners being almost excluded. The number of examinations was stringently cut as well.

The epidemic did wane a little after the reduction of the number of students, but it soon flared up again, as severely as before. Semmelweis could not accept the commission's report that the disease of childbed fever was due to rough examinations, for it was evident that the birth process itself was far rougher than any examination would be. Yet he had no specific remedy to propose.

He was "convinced," he wrote later in *Die Ætiologie*, "that the greater mortality in the First Clinic originated from a cause, endemic, but still unknown, sought for by me in vain." Professor Klein was equally adamant in his conviction that the trouble came from the outside.

Chapter 7

The Solution

IN A WAY the enforced vacation which followed his demotion may have been a good thing, for it gave Semmelweis time to think and particularly to evaluate the work he had done and the knowledge he had gained from his studies of midwifery and childbed fever. One fact stood out above all the others. Dr. Boër had studied in England and had applied English methods when he assumed charge of the Lying-in Hospital. Under his regime there had been no fever of importance. Semmelweis also undoubtedly knew from his reading that British obstetricians had evolved some means of controlling the spread of the fever. It was logical for him to conclude that the place to pursue his studies during the following years, until he once more became Assistant, was in England and Ireland, where, more than anywhere else is the world, puerperal fever seemed to have been prevented to a large degree.

With characteristic enthusiasm he threw himself into the study of English during the winter of 1846-47, and announced his intention of studying at the great lying-in hospital of Dublin.

This statement makes it seem probable that he had read of the work of Collins while Master of the Rotunda. It is a little hard to understand why Semmelweis did not immediately spot the importance of Collins' work, but it is likely that his failure to do so arose from his rejection of the theory of contagion. As he wrote:

That childbed fever is not a contagious disease and that the disease is not carried from bed to bed by a *contagium,* [undoubtedly he means here through the air] we shall express here as our conviction. . . . For the present, the observation will suffice that, if childbed fever be a contagious disease, the sporadic cases of disease among the puerperae of the Second Clinic [in contradistinction to the First, where they frequently became ill in rows] would be sufficient to make the sporadic case an epidemic among the puerperae, by extension of the *contagium* from bed to bed.

It seems likely that the later English obstetricians and probably also Oliver Wendell Holmes recognized that what they called a *contagium* was actually a tangible something which could be carried on the hands of the operator, but Semmelweis was probably not familiar with this distinction. It has been fairly well established that he did not come in contact with the report of Holmes, nor was Holmes familiar with Semmelweis' work until many years afterward.

Then Dr. Breit was offered the Professorship of Obstetrics at the University of Tübingen, and Semmelweis was assured of regaining his old position in a few weeks. Overjoyed at his good fortune he set out with two friends for Venice for a short vacation. Full of enthusiasm and happy once more, he threw himself into the holiday, visited the art treasures, and reveled in their beauty.

On March 20, 1847, he returned to Vienna and was immediately installed once more in his old post as Assistant in the First Obstetrical Clinic. Only one thing dimmed the pleasure of the restoration; during his absence his friend Jakob Kolletschka, the professor of Forensic Medicine, only 43 years old, had died of a scalpel wound sustained while performing an autopsy. This was a well known danger of dissection, not limited to Vienna, for Oliver Wendell Holmes mentioned it in his treatise on puerperal fever some four years before, and many another pathological anatomist had died just as Kolletschka did, demonstrating anatomy to an awkward student. The knife had slipped and wounded his fingers. Infection had set in, followed by pyemia.

Pyemia! It was a dread word in the deadhouses, the constant fear of all those who dissected. A prick of the knife, sometimes only of a needle used in sewing up the bodies, a wound that often went unnoticed. The next day there was redness about the wound, the beginning of a throbbing pain, ominous red streaks up along the arm following the paths of the lymphatic vessels. And then in spite of everything that could be done, there was often fever, swelling, delirium, the racing pulse of profound toxemia, the short stertorous breathing of pneumonia, the stiffness of the neck from inflamed meninges, the swollen abdomen from peritonitis, and finally, if death were delayed that long, multiple abscesses all over the body.

Semmelweis himself was so impressed by Kolletschka's fate that he described it minutely in *Die Ætiologie:*

The history of his illness was as follows: Kolletschka, Professor of Forensic Medicine, frequently participated with his pupils in the performance of medico-legal autopsies; during such an exercise, he was stuck in the finger by a student with a knife which was used during the post-mortem, in which finger I do not recall. Professor Kolletschka then became ill with lymphangitis and phlebitis in the same upper extremity and died, during my absence in Venice, of a bilateral pleuritis, pericarditis, peritonitis, and meningitis, and some days before his death a metastasis formed in one eye.

Kolletschka was dead! His mourning for his friend could not still the instinct of the scientist within Semmelweis as he read the familiar words of Rokitansky's description of the autopsy: Peritonitis! Pleuritis! Meningitis! Multiple abscesses! How the words must have pounded in his brain.

For those were familiar words; familiar from descriptions of other autopsies, upon women who had died from puerperal fever!

In Kolletschka's case the wound has been incurred at the autopsy table. In others it had been during surgical operations upon abscesses and erysipelas. But the findings were still the same as in childbed fever.

Surgical pyemia! Pathologist's pyemia! Childbed fever, no less truly a pyemia! The parts of the puzzle fell suddenly into place in his mind:

Still animated by my visit to the Venetian treasure houses of Art, still more agitated by the report of Kolletschka's death, there was forced upon my mind with irresistible clarity in this excited state the identity of this disease, of which Kolletschka died, with that from which I had seen so many hundred puerperae die. The puerperae died likewise of phlebitis, lymphangitis, peritonitis, pleuritis, pericarditis, and metastases were also formed in them. Day and night this picture of Kolletschka's disease pursued me, and with ever increasing determination, I was obliged to acknowledge the identity of the disease, from which Kolletschka died, with that disease of which I saw so many puerperae die.

From the identity of the pathological findings in the cadavers of the newborn with the pathological findings in the women, who died from childbed fever, we had concluded earlier and we think rightly, that the newborn died also of childbed fever, or in other words, the newborn died of the same disease as did the puerperae. Since we came upon the identical results in the pathological findings in Kolletschka as in the puerperae, then the conclusion that Kolletschka died of the same disease, from which I had seen so many hundred puerperae die, likewise was justified. The exciting cause of Professor Kolletschka's illness was known, that is to say, the wound produced by the autopsy knife was contaminated at the same time by cadaveric material. Not the wound, but the contamination of the wound by cadaveric material was the cause of death. Kolletschka was not the first to die in this fashion. I must acknowledge, if Kolletschka's disease and the disease from which I saw so many puerperae die, are identical, then in the puerperae it must be produced by the self-same engendering cause, which produced it in Kolletschka. In Kolletschka, the specific agent was cadaveric particles, which were introduced into his vascular system [circulation]. I must ask myself the question: Did the cadaveric particles make their way into the vascular systems of the individuals, whom I had seen die of an identical disease? This question I answer in the affirmative.

Because of the anatomic trend in the Vienna Medical School, the Professors, Assistants and students have frequent opportunity to come in contact with cadavers. That the cadaveric particles clinging to the hands are not entirely removed by the ordinary method of washing the hands with soap, is shown by the cadaveric odor, which the hands retain for a longer or shorter time. During the examination of gravidae [pregnant women], parturients [women in labor], and puerperae, the hand contaminated by cadaveric particles is brought into contact with the genitals of these individuals, and hence the possibility of absorption, and by means of absorption, introduction of cadaveric particles into the vascular system of these individuals is postulated, and by this means the same disease is produced in these puerperae, which we saw in Kolletschka.

If the hypothesis is correct, that the hand-borne cadaveric particles produce the same disease in puerperae, which the cadaveric particles clinging to the knife caused in Kolletschka, then, if by a chemical effect they may be completely destroyed on the hand, and thereby during examinations of gravidae, parturients, and puerperae, whose genitals may be brought directly in contact with the fingers and not with the cadaveric material, this disease can be prevented to the extent that it is dependent upon the effect of cadaveric particles carried by the examining finger. From the first this seemed to me more than likely, since the fact was known to me that decaying organic matter brought in contact with living organisms produced in them a putrefactive process.

In spite of the profusion of words, characteristic of Semmelweis' writings, no logic could be more direct and no conclusion more definite than this. The identity of puerperal fever with the pyemia following autopsy wounds and surgical wounds came to Semmelweis suddenly when he read of Kolletschka's death and autopsy, but his far-reaching conclusions concerning etiology were slowly evolved over a period of about two months. Actually, of course, the mental processes which led to the correct conclusion had been going on during his years of study and observation in the First Clinic, particularly under the stimulus of that always recurring question: why was the mortality so much higher in the First Clinic than in the Second? Now of course the explanation was simple: in the First Clinic the students carried the cadaveric particles to the patients on their hands, while in the Second Clinic the midwives, who performed no dissections, were not so contaminated. The physicians of the Second Clinic—Professor Bartsch and his Assistant, Dr. von Arneth—very seldom visited the pathology laboratory. Semmelweis now recalled that the previous Assistant in the Second Clinic, Dr. Zipfel, had worked diligently at pathological and anatomical studies; during his tenure the childbed-fever mortality in the Second Clinic had risen to a higher rate than it had achieved before or since.

And now many other things were explained. Why did the mothers in the First Division so often sicken in rows? Simply because they were examined by the students, the Professor, and the Assistant in rows.

Why did the epidemic of fever temporarily decrease when the foreign students were sent away? Semmelweis himself explains this:

The foreigners come to Vienna, in order to complete a medical education already obtained in other universities. They attend the pathological and forensic courses in the General Hospital, they take courses in pathological anatomy, operative instruction on the cadaver in surgery, obstetrics, and ophthalmology, they visit the medical and surgical wards, etc., in a word, they spend their time as efficiently and as profitably as possible, but in this way they have manifold opportunities to contaminate their hands with decomposed animal-organic matter, and therefore it is not surprising that the foreigners, busy at the same time in the lying-in hospital, were dangerous to the patients.

The native students, he goes on to point out, took their courses in a more leisurely fashion and had less occasion to dissect than the foreigners while attending the obstetrical clinic.

The lack of childbed fever among the street-births was also easily explained now. Having had their children outside the hospital, the women did not need to be examined and no cadaveric material was brought to them.

The recognition of his own agency in causing so many deaths came bitterly home to Semmelweis now. During Breit's brief second tenure as Assistant, the mortality rate had fallen decisively, as low as 1.92% in February. With the restoration of Semmelweis, it had risen again, reaching 18.27% in April. The difference could be explained only by Semmelweis' greater diligence in his early-morning work in the pathology laboratory and in his examination of patients thereafter.

What a shock it must have been to him to realize that he had sedulously carried death where he meant to bring life!

It seemed definite to Semmelweis, in the first flush of discovery, that the whole story of puerperal fever lay in this question of cadaveric particles which could not always be seen, but could be identified by their characteristic odor. Logically, too, anything which destroyed the odor destroyed the particles.

On May 24, Semmelweis was summoned to the home of Ferdinand von Hebra; Frau Hebra's pains had begun. He had not worked in the pathology laboratory since his discovery had taken form in his mind. Now he took additional precautions, scrubbing his hands with the greatest care, cleansing the instruments he might need, changing to clothes that carried no taint of the dissecting chamber. Then he hurried to the house at No. 19 Alserstrasse, opposite the General Hospital, and saw his friend's young wife safely through her confinement, crying out triumphantly, "It's a boy!" The mother's recovery was rapid and uneventful; no symptom of the dreaded fever appeared; and Hans von Hebra lived to become a professor of dermatology like his father and to boast that he had been born under the care of Semmelweis.

The methods he had taken to insure Frau Hebra's safety, Semmelweis well knew, could not be applied to the problem of the Lying-in Hospital. Students would continue to dissect, and soap and water alone, he proved to his own satisfaction, were ineffectual against the cadaveric odor. He began to search for something which would destroy the poisonous material which students and faculty were bringing to mothers in labor. Chlorine, we have seen was used by Collins almost twenty years before in fumigating the lying-in wards of the Rotunda. Discovered by Scheele in 1774, it had also been used in the purification of water by Morveau of France and Cruikshank of England in 1800. In 1819 Labarraque was the first to employ a chlorine solution for purposes of disinfection. It was this well established antiseptic which Semmelweis chose for his experiment:

In order to destroy the cadaveric particles adhering to the hand, although I cannot now recall the date, but about the middle of May, 1847 [probably at the end of May, according to von Waldheim], I began to use Chlorina liquida, with which I and every student were obliged to wash our hands before making an examination. After some time, I abandoned the Chlorina liquida, because of its high price and changed to the considerably cheaper chlorinated lime. In May 1847, in the latter half of which the chlorine-washings were introduced, there still died 36 or 12.24% out of 294 puerperae. . . .

The system of prophylaxis which Semmelweis introduced into the regular obstetric practice in the First Clinic in May, 1847, was simple. Bowls of the chlorine solution, each with some clean sand in the bottom which could be used for scrubbing, were placed at the entrance to the clinic through which the students and teachers came for the classes and for the other manifold activities of the division. Posted conspicuously about in the ward, too, were placards of directions:

All students or doctors who enter the wards for the purpose of making an examination must wash their hands thoroughly in a solution of chlorinated lime which will be placed in convenient basins near the entrance of the wards. This disinfection is considered sufficient for this visit. Between examinations the hands must be washed in soap and water.

He had himself tested the efficacy of this chlorine washing by its ability to remove from his own reeking hands the smell of the dissecting rooms, and however unpleasant the solution was, there was no doubting its efficacy in destroying the cadaveric matter, which he was certain now was the cause of the disease.

In the hospital the prophylaxis was a success from the beginning. In June the mortality was only 2.38%, in July 1.20%, and in August 1.89%. These were figures not attained in the First Division of the Lying-in Hospital since the time of Boër, and they brought the death-rate for the first time into close approximation with that in the Second Division.

The news of Semmelweis' great innovation spread rapidly through the hospital. Hebra, Rokitansky, Skoda, and the Chief Physician, Haller, heard his account of the discovery and were certain that he had at last hit upon the solution of the problem. But Klein stood adamant against his Assistant's revelation. And when Skoda, seeing that Semmelweis found no understanding from his chief, proposed a commission to investigate the matter, Klein effectively squelched the proposal as representing unjustifiable interference in the affairs of his department. The feud between Skoda and Klein which resulted from this event could not but have evil results for Semmelweis. Thereafter Klein was his enemy.

With the increase of students in the fall term, the mortality rose again. In spite of all his efforts, Semmelweis could not supervise everything himself, and the chlorine washing was not popular with those who did not stop to consider its value. The chemical irritated the hands and the smell soon permeated the building, although it should have been a welcome substitute for the odor of the cadaver soaked into the walls by the passing of many generations of students fresh from the dissecting rooms. In September, one rebellious student amused himself by ridiculing the Assistant's "hobby horse" and deliberately neglected to take antiseptic precautions. In that month 5.23% died. Semmelweis discovered the offender and assailed him with scathing words. Thereafter there was no more ridicule, although carelessness, deliberate or otherwise, continued to some degree.

It was perhaps at this time that Semmelweis conceived of and petitioned for a law which he mentioned several times in Die Ætiologie. Believing, rightly enough, that it was better to prevent contamination than to remove it, he desired a regulation to be passed to the effect that medical students occupied in the Lying-in Hospital be prohibited from engaging in any dissection whatsoever. His petition, appearing, as was inevitable, before Profesor Klein, was doomed to an early death. Klein, on his accession to the directorship in 1822, had been responsible for the introduction of work on the cadaver into the obstetric curriculum. Under his predecessor Boër, obstetric instruction had been carried out with the "phantom," a body machine with an artificial uterus and pelvic canal, through which dolls were pushed to show the mechanics of the birth process.

If Semmelweis' petition served any purpose, it was to increase the hatred which Klein now held for him. He could have felt no other sentiment for the brilliant young Assistant who dared to defy the traditions of the "epidemic theory" so dear to Klein's own heart. And even more galling, Semmelweis had stated openly that something inside the Krankenhaus itself caused the fever, something which, statistically, could be proved to have arrived with Klein himself. There must have been a powerful force of envy burning inside this pompous little man who had managed to have Boër thrown out of the chair of obstetrics so that he himself might occupy it. And there must have rankled in his mind the incontrovertible fact that where he lost many women, Boër had lost few.

And now came a bumptious Hungarian who said there was a reason for this loss, a reason which had been actually introduced by Klein: frequent dissection by students and professors in the pathological laboratory.

Klein assumed a lack of interest in the First Division, but this did not mean that he had given up opposition to Semmelweis, for he had other ways of keeping in touch with events in the Lying-in Hospital. Midwives, dissatisfied or disgruntled with Semmelweis' sometimes highhanded insistence upon rigid antisepsis, knew where they could find a ready ear for their complaints—not always truthful ones either—and perhaps a reward. And students who resented the Assistant's demands of unswerving obedience to the rules knew where they could find a sympathetic ear in a high place. They would not have been students if they had not taken advantage of that knowledge. In the city-within-a-building which is any large hospital and medical school, there were many ways in which Klein could learn exactly what his Assistant was doing, without actually appearing to take any interest at all.

From his high place Professor Klein continually pulled the petty strings of jealousy, hampering Semmelweis in a hundred ways, depriving him of needed supplies, dropping disparaging remarks during lectures to the students, inserting damaging opinions into the political caucuses which were so important in determining the policies of the hospital and medical school.

There was little that Klein could do directly, however, as long as things went smoothly in Semmelweis' department. And Semmelweis, himself, conscious of the antagonism of his superior, was careful not to give further cause for hatred to the plump, vindictive Professor of Obstetrics.

Meanwhile Semmelweis' friends in the Krankenhaus rejoiced in his success and urged him to publish it to the world. But the tradition of the scientist was strong within him. He was convinced, but before he could convince the world he must accumulate evidence which, however incontrovertible he might think it, would be equally so to men whose thinking was narrowed and cramped by dogma. So Semmelweis went patiently about his work, serene in the confidence that anything so true as his *Lehre*, his doctrine, must become known merely by its own lifesaving properties.

And there he made a serious mistake, for no great discovery has ever been immediately accepted. Rather, in medicine, it seems that the reverse is true, and every one must go through a period of trial and even censure before what seems the obvious truth is recognized generally. Perhaps this is best in the final analysis, because such opposition has throttled many a false doctrine before it could be widely accepted by the credulous and exploited by the charlatan. But such slow acceptance prevents the real discoveries from being known and widely accepted earlier, and many lives are thus sacrificed needlessly.

Chapter 8

The First Trial, Vienna

IN THE summer of 1847, two young medical students from Heidelberg arrived in Vienna. They were Adolf Kussmaul and Edward Bronner. The former has left an account of their six-month visit in his *Jugenderrinnerungen eines alten Arztes* (Youthful Memories of an Old Physician). On their arrival they found the medical school in recess; only Hebra's course in dermatology was being given. They attended this course, devoting much of their remaining time to examining the buildings and equipment of the great hospital and finding much to praise. They marveled, too, at the amount of medical material available in the hospital, where yearly 3000 childbirths took place and 1600 post-mortems were performed. Kussmaul found his greatest interest in the inadequate rooms of the morgue, where he observed about three hundred of Rokitansky's deft autopsies.

With the opening of the fall semester, Bronner and Kussmaul enrolled in Semmelweis' course in obstetrical surgery and found it "wholly superior." Kussmaul's account includes a description of Semmelweis as he was at this time which is of interest:

He is more than medium height, broad and strongly built, his face round with somewhat prominent cheek bones, his forehead high and his hair rather thin for his years; he has remarkably fleshy and dextrous hands. He is of a lively temperament and has a great capacity and willingness to work. He has a warm and kindly heart and is conscientious to an extreme degree.

As soon as Semmelweis learned that both his new students had been assistants to Naegele of Heidelberg, whom he deeply respected, he displayed marked friendliness toward them and did all in his power to assist them. After they completed his course he managed to secure for them permission, much desired but at that time not easily won, to practice in the Lying-in Hospital for six weeks. There they found him constantly kind and helpful, always ready to lend a hand, even at the cost of needed rest. Klein, on the other hand, appeared to them an ineffectual creature, indifferent to his duties as professor and clinician, and possessed of a strong and scarcely concealed prejudice against foreign students. To his Assistant's struggle against childbed fever, Klein gave, they could see, no cooperation.

It was perhaps fortunate for Semmelweis that in the autumn of 1847 he had about him such sympathetic observers as these two Heidelbergers. For, with his prophylaxis in operation and everything apparently going perfectly in the fight against childbed fever, disaster struck. In October, twelve women in a row of beds became suddenly ill with a virulent form of the disease, and of these twelve, eleven died.

It was a body-blow to the theory of cadaveric particles, for the prophylaxis had been rigorously observed when the students who entered the ward began the examinations. Semmelweis himself had been with them. Yet eleven women, all examined on the same day, died shortly afterward with the typical signs of childbed fever. None of them, it seemed, could possibly have come in contact with cadaveric material. And it was even more of a blow to the system of prophylaxis, for apparently some poisonous substance had reached these women in spite of the hand-washing which Semmelweis insisted upon.

Here was the proof that Klein needed to controvert Semmelweis' theory and brand the prophylaxis as useless. But the years Semmelweis had spent in discovering the cause of the fever had taught him to approach such a problem logically. He was sure himself that material brought to the lying-in mothers on the hands of the operators and examiners caused their deaths; therefore, something must have reached them after the chlorine handwashing with which the morning visit to the wards began. The logical place to look for the cause was in the first patient examined that morning, for, while she had not taken the fever, eleven of the next twelve in the row with her had died. And there he found the answer:

In order to destroy the cadaveric matter adhering to the hands, every examiner must wash his hands in a solution of chlorinated lime as soon as he entered the labor room, and since the students had no opportunity to pollute their hands anew with cadaveric particles, I considered it sufficient if the students should wash their hands once with the chlorinated lime solution. On account of the large number of deliveries occurring in one year in the First Clinic, only infrequently was there but one parturient in the labor room, and as a rule there were several in labor at once. For the purposes of instruction, all the parturients, as they lay alongside one another, were examined along the rows, and I considered it sufficient to have the hands washed with soapy water in between examinations; I considered that washing with chlorine water between examinations was superfluous, since in the labor room, after the hand had been cleansed of the cadaveric particles clinging to it, it could not be contaminated with them again.

In October 1847, there was admitted a parturient suffering from a foully discharging medullary carcinoma (cancer) of the uterus; to her was assigned as a labor bed the bed at which the visit always began.

After the examination of this parturient, we examiners merely washed our hands with soap; the result was that 11, of the 12

women delivered along with her, died. The foul discharge from
this medullary carcinoma was not destroyed by the soapy water,
the ichor [fluid from a sore or wound] was carried over by the
examinations to the other parturients, and so the childbed fever
was multiplied.

Thus childbed fever is caused not only by cadaveric particles
clinging to the hand, but also by ichorous discharges originating
in living organisms; for that reason, the hands of the examiner
must be cleansed with chlorine water, not only after handling
cadavers, but likewise after examining patients, wherein the
hands may be contaminated by ichor, before proceeding to the
examination of a second individual.

The rule developed from this sad experience we observed subsequently, and childbed fever was no longer spread by the transfer of ichor from one patient to another by the examining
fingers.

Certainly nothing could be clearer or simpler than this
description in Semmelweis' own words of the way in which
puerperal fever could be caused not only by soiled hands
from the cadaver, but from any infected source. Unfortunately this frank statement was not published for several
years, and by that time the idea of cadaveric particles as the
only cause of the fever had become so steeped into the minds
of those who, either through ignorance or through intention,
did not try to learn more about it, that it was to hinder for
many years the spread of his doctrine and cause him much
unhappiness.

Semmelweis' new orders, that everyone must wash his
hands in antiseptic solution after each examination, stirred
up a storm of protest. His critics seized upon the incident to
assail him for what they considered his silly theories. They
found a thousand objections to the chlorine prophylaxis: that
it was not good for the skin; that the chlorine remaining on
the hands was injurious to the birth passages of the mothers;
that the washing took so much time there was none left for
the examinations and routine work of the wards. But Semmelweis went serenely on, paying no attention to those who
sneered, descending like a tornado upon any luckless student
who came to the examination with the faintest odor of the
dissecting rooms on his hands.

In November a new experience led to an additional conclusion. The fever flared up in that month, with eleven
deaths, and eight more to follow in early December. At first
at a loss, Semmelweis soon explained the tragedy. A patient

with a discharging carious left knee-joint had been admitted to the lying-in ward. Her reproductive tract was completely healthy, hence the examining finger could have carried no infection to other patients. But the exhalations from the diseased knee were so considerable that the close air of the ward was permeated by it and the infection conveyed in that way. Thereafter, Semmelweis saw that such cases were carefully isolated.

Only a small powerful group of reactionaries, headed by Klein and Professor Rosas, the ophthalmologist, fought consistently against the recognition of Semmelweis' theories. They were the embodiment of reaction, this little group, always ready to exercise their powerful influence against the aspirations of any young man of ability and originality who exhibited a spark of independent thought.

The reasons for their violent opposition to Semmelweis can only be conjectured. Certainly his brusque manner and his refusal to bow down to the entrenched forces of didacticism and dogma which ruled Vienna made him unpopular with this group. Undoubtedly they envied him the position he was achieving in the medical life of the University as a result of his momentous discovery. Perhaps, too, Klein foresaw the day when he might be edged out of his own chair, just as he had usurped the position of the far more capable Boër years before. It is possible that they were really sincere in their refusal to accept theories that had not yet stood the test of time; certainly they had opposed others before Semmelweis. Skoda had found as much opposition when he first began to develop his ideas of percussion and auscultation and to demonstrate the relation between the physical signs of disease discovered at the bedside and the final evidence at the post-mortem table.

Certainly if Semmelweis was depressed by the opposition of the reactionaries—and he was more likely to be angered, for he sometimes fell into fits of impotent fury at delay and incompetence—he was cheered by the way his prophylaxis was taken up by the foreign postgraduate students of midwifery.

Vienna was then coming into the position which it was to occupy for another fifty years as the center of medical knowledge on the Continent, if not in the world. The pick of foreign students flocked there. Along with Kussmaul and Bronner of Heidelberg, came F. H. C. Routh of London, Stendrichs of Amsterdam, Schwarz, a friend and protégé of Michaelis of Kiel, and Wieger of Strasbourg. All observed the working of the prophylaxis, the undoubted protection it gave against childbed fever which they had almost come to accept in their own clinics as inevitable; all were voluble in praise of its discoverer and of his marvelous ability as an obstetric operator. His courses were among the best attended in the University, almost as well as those of Rokitansky and Skoda. But unlike Klein, these two scientists did not resent the success of their young friend and they strove in every way to further the advancement of his career.

Searching always for other possible sources of infection, Semmelweis soon widened the application of his prophylaxis to include the washing of everything which came in contact with the patient, such as catheters, bedpans, and instruments. He insisted that only clean sheets should be used for cases in labor, and made the midwives wash their hands whenever they did anything for a patient. All of this caused more objection, but no one could withstand the incontrovertible fact that the mortality from puerperal fever was falling steadily under this regimen.

His friends continually urged him to publish his results and make his method known to the world. Again and again they begged him to publish articles, to appear before medical societies, but he refused. He hated the pen, he argued, and he was a poor talker, the latter statement certainly not true. He was satisfied that his doctrine must spread of itself, apparently unaware that the truth spreads slowest of all. To him the proof was complete, simple, incontrovertible. He could not conceive that anyone could fail to see it, that anyone should refuse to believe the truth once it spread of its own power through the obstetrical world.

It is difficult to understand this reluctance of Semmelweis to write and speak of his work. Was it the natural reluctance of a scientist to publish the results of what might be regarded still as an experiment? Yet he himself certainly did not regard it as an experiment any longer. His retiring nature abhorred anything that resembled self-aggrandizement, yet he was so filled with his work, so cognizant of its importance in saving lives, that he could hardly have refrained for that reason.

More logical as a cause but certainly not sensible on Semmelweis' part may have been his honest opinion that his doctrine could best be spread by those of his students who went out into the world to apply his methods in other clinics and other cities, and by the midwives trained in the Second Clinic where the Assistant, von Arneth, was now a firm believer in the chlorine disinfection. Whatever the reason, Semmelweis refused to write or speak about his doctrine, and in so doing closed the greatest avenue of possible dissemination, annoying his friends at the same time.

But one means was open. The foreign obstetricians in his classes were men of experience and training. Their judgment had matured to the point where they could recognize the importance to obstetrics of this new method of prophylaxis, and they saw the results with their own eyes. Most of them were loyal to Semmelweis and anxious to see his discovery publicized.

With his permission some of these students began to write long letters of report to their home schools and clinics, describing the doctrine of infection elaborated by Semmelweis and the method of prophylaxis by means of chloride of lime. Routh wrote home to England; Stendrichs to Tilanus of Amsterdam; Schwarz to Michaelis of Kiel. Arneth, Assistant in the Midwives' Clinic, knew English better than Semmelweis did and therefore undertook to write to the great British obstetrician, Sir James Y. Simpson, in Edinburgh. Kussmaul, one of Semmelweis' closest friends among the foreign observers, wrote enthusiastically to Naegele of Heidelberg. Others in the small circle of adherents wrote also, and with each letter that went forth, Semmelweis thought he saw his doctrine accepted in yet another hospital.

Skoda took up the cause as well, writing to his friend and patron Nadherny of Prague and asking that the latter use his influence as president of the medical faculty at Prague to introduce there this happy discovery. Nadherny complied by communicating the news to the Prague faculty; then he sent Skoda's letter on to his son-in-law, Hofrat Kiwisch von Rotterau, Professor of Obstetrics at Würzburg, who had himself written an extensive work on puerperal fever. In this secondhand manner of disseminating his doctrine, however ill-advised a course it may have been, Semmelweis had many and able supporters. Nevertheless, Skoda's letter was later to become a focus of criticism, for the Prague obstetricians were offended that they had received no direct announcement of the discovery.

Ferdinand von Hebra also lent his aid in spreading the doctrine, in an even more telling fashion. Like Skoda, he was disgusted with Klein's short-sighted policy in rejecting Semmelweis' discovery. He determined to encourage his friend and to win recognition for him in spite of Klein. Before Christmas Hebra surprised Semmelweis by publishing the following article in the December issue of the *Journal of the Royal Imperial Society of Physicians in Vienna:*

The Editor of this Journal feels it is his duty to communicate to the medical profession, in view of the prevalence of puerperal fever in all lying-in hospitals, the following observations made by Dr. Semmelweis, Assistant in the First Obstetric Clinic in the General Hospital of this city.

Dr. Semmelweis, who has been already for five years at the hospital, has become thoroughly instructed at the dissecting table as well as at the beds of the patients in the various branches of the healing art. For the last two years he has devoted special attention to the subject of midwifery, and has undertaken the task of inquiring into the causes which lie at the basis of the prevailing epidemic puerperal processes. On this subject nothing has been left untested, and everything which could exercise an injurious influence had been carefully removed.

By daily visits to an institution of pathology and anatomy Dr. Semmelweis had learnt what were the injurious influences produced by filthy and putrid fluids upon even unwounded portions of the body of individuals engaged in post-mortem examinations. These observations aroused in him the thought that perhaps in the lying-in hospitals the pregnant and parturient patients might be inoculated by the accoucheur [obstetrician] himself, and that puerperal fever was in most cases nothing else than cadaveric infection.

In order to test this opinion, it was laid down as a rule in the First Obstetric Clinic that everyone, before making an examination of a pregnant woman, must first wash his hands in an aqueous solution of chloride of lime (Chloratis calcis unc. I, Aqua fontana lib. duas). The result was surprisingly favourable: for during the months of April and May, when this rule had not yet come into force out of 100 cases of labor there were 18 deaths, the number of deaths in the following months up to November 26, only amounted to 47 out of 1,547 cases, that is to say the mortality amounted to 2.45 per cent.

From this circumstance the problem is perhaps solved, why in schools for midwives the proportion of the prevalent mortality is so favourable in comparison with that of the institutions devoted to the training of students of medicine. An exception is the Maternité of Paris where, as is well known, post-mortem examinations are undertaken by the pupil-midwives.

Three distinct facts of experience may perhaps still further confirm the conviction just expressed and even extend still further its scope. Dr. Semmelweis believes that he can prove that:

1. Owing to careless washing some student engaged in dissection caused the loss of several patients in the month of September;

2. In the month of October, owing to frequent examinations of a patient in labour, who suffered from a foul-smelling medullary sarcoma of the uterus, when washing was not practised. Also finally:

3. Owing to a filthy discharge from an ulcer of the leg in one of the patients, several women who were confined at the same time were infected.

Thus, therefore, *the conveyance of a foul exudation from a living organism may be one cause which produces the puerperal process.*

In publishing these experiences we invite the Directors of all lying-in institutions, some of whom Dr. Semmelweis has already made acquainted with these most important observations, to contribute the results of their investigations either to support or refute them. (Sinclair's translation.)

In this article Hebra definitely challenged the critics of Semmelweis to produce statistics to disprove the efficacy of his method.

Thus, in a publication of wide circulation, Semmelweis' doctrine was first presented to the medical world, and, despite several minor errors, its central principle was stated unequivocally: that puerperal fever, while usually a cadaveric infection in Vienna, was sometimes an infection from a putrid exudation or discharge in a living organism.

In view of the clear-cut statement of the methods of infection set forth by Hebra and in the letters of Semmelweis' students to other centers, it is hard to see how his meaning could have been twisted, even by those who hated him, into the statement that pueperal fever was caused only by matter transmitted from the dissecting room to the delivery room. But seize upon this pretext they did to try to discredit him with those who were not fully conversant with the principles he outlined. Thus a tremendous controversy began to arise.

Several of the letters written by Semmelweis' students were not answered. The first reply received was an answer to the letter from F. H. von Arneth to Sir James Y. Simpson. The famous accoucheur wrote promptly but tartly, completely rejecting Semmelweis' discoveries. Semmelweis later wrote of Simpson's letter:

This letter was filled with abuse; Simpson said that without the letter [Arneth's] he knew in what a lamentable condition midwifery in Germany, and especially Vienna, still remained; he knew for certain that the cause of the high mortality lay only in the unbounded carelessness with which patients were treated; as for example, when they put a healthy lying-in woman into the same bed in which another patient had just died, without changing the bedclothes or linen.

Semmelweis' extreme sensitivity on behalf of his beloved doctrine probably led to his statement that Simpson's letter was abusive; more likely it was written with the honest acerbity of a man protesting against conditions which he thought terrible. Simpson went on to say that the Viennese obstetricians must be totally ignorant of British obstetrical literature, or they would have been aware that the British had for a long time been convinced that puerperal fever was a contagious disease and that they had used chlorine disinfection to prevent it. Here again we see the old misunderstanding about the doctrine of contagion as opposed to Semmelweis' docrine of direct transmission of a palpable substance in the form of cadaveric particles or discharges from wounds, including the lochia from other cases of puerperal fever. It is apparent that Simpson, then preoccupied with his chloroform experiments, wholly missed the point of Arneth's communication.

Semmelweis concluded: "This letter did not make us feel disposed to continue the correspondence with Simpson."

In 1850, shortly before Arneth himself lectured on the Semmelweis theory in Edinburgh, Simpson published an article in which he admitted the value of the Semmelweis prophylaxis; he had come to recognize the undeniable importance of preventing the entry of foreign matter into the bodies of parturient women and to realize the difference between the Semmelweis doctrine and the contagion theory popular in England.

The initial adverse reactions of Simpson and other prominent obstetricians wounded the sensitive soul of Semmelweis and possibly contributed to his reluctance to publish abroad his researches and their far-reaching conclusions. But not all the scientists of the day by any means closed their eyes to the light of the "puerperal sun," as Semmelweis called it later, "that shone in Vienna in 1847." Tilanus of Amsterdam replied favorably on March 9, 1848, though not committing himself completely to the Semmelweis doctrine. Kiwisch of Würzburg hurried to Vienna in 1848 to talk with Semmelweis and observe the new prophylaxis at first hand. And in answer to Schwarz' letter, Michaelis of Kiel wrote on March 18:

When I received your letter, I was again in the greatest distress. Our institution had been closed on account of puerperal fever from the first of July to the first of November. The first three patients then admitted fell ill, one of them died and the other two were just saved. Your communication gave me some encouragement for the first time. I at once introduced your method of chlorine disinfection into our institution. Our hands used to smell all day long of the dissected cadaver in spite of repeated washing, but the chlorine disinfection has put an end to that. Since the introduction of your method not a single case of labor attended either by myself or my pupils has shown the slightest degree of fever with the exception of one in February. I therefore thank you for your communication with all my heart; you have perhaps saved our institution from destruction. I beg of you to greet Dr. Semmelweis on my behalf and to offer him my thanks: he has perhaps made a great discovery. You are aware that puerperal fever broke out here for the first time in 1834, and that was about the time when students were required to make regular examinations of the patients. This circumstance may also have relation to the etiology.

The results during the spring of 1848 were striking enough to convince, it would seem, even the most biased observer. Under Semmelweis' careful superintendence the death-rate fell steadily. In March there were no puerperal fever deaths in the First Clinic. In the ten months which had passed since chlorine-washing had been introduced, out of 2670 patients only 67 had died, a number often formerly exceeded in the First Clinic in the course of a single month.

All this encouraged Semmelweis, but he was saddened that the reactionaries still held out against him and that, in spite of the knowledge he had brought out into the open, women still died in lying-in institutions throughout Europe from a thoroughly preventable disease, puerperal fever.

In the summer, too, he was to be grieved by news from Kiel. Michaelis, who had been one of the first to try his method and give it his approval, committed suicide. He had delivered, in the summer of 1847, a young cousin of whom he was very fond. Shortly afterward she developed the fever and died. In the light of the knowledge he had received from Vienna, Michaelis realized that he alone had been responsible for her death, that he had brought the deadly infection to her with his own hands. This, along with the knowledge of how many women he must have infected in the same way, began to prey upon his mind. Michaelis cracked under the strain and one day he thrust himself beneath the wheels of a train in Hamburg.

Semmelweis himself had known the agony of the same terrible thought. When he realized the truth concerning the conveyance of puerperal fever, he had to realize as well that he had sent many a woman to her death. "God only knows the number of women whom I have consigned prematurely to the grave," he wrote, "for I have occupied myself with the cadaver to a degree reached by few obstetricians." He could enter fully into the horror that had possessed Michaelis.

Chapter 9

The Victory of Reaction

THE YEAR 1847, in which Semmelweis arrived at a triumphant solution to his problem, saw problems of another sort drawing toward a crisis throughout the Austrian Empire and all of Europe. The forces of revolution were everywhere in ferment. Hungary especially, land of fierce patriotism where lesser racial groups glowered under the arrogant superiority of the Magyars, who in turn resented the patronage of Vienna, was kindling into fire. And, but for the diversity of the flames which composed it, this fire might have burned its way to freedom.

Joseph II, years before, had determined to improve the conditions of his Hungarian subjects by forcing Germanic culture upon this intensely nationalistic people. His aims were good, but his methods were autocratic; where he would have created reform, he bred antagonism; and where he would have brought about unity, he fostered discord. A succession of Austrian rulers had continued the policies of Joseph, influenced by the directing mind of Metternich. Metternich preached stability; his method had been to set peoples against each other, all the while maintaining like a juggler the balance between the diverse peoples who made up the Empire. He had managed to maintain the delicate balance througout the long reign of Francis I and for more than a decade under the feeble Ferdinand. Now the scales began to tip.

It was logical that the Hungarians, the most intensely patriotic of the peoples who made up the Empire, should be the first to strive to throw off the yoke of Metternich. There had been risings in Galicia and Ruthenia the year before, but these had been put down after brief struggles. Hungary, the patriots assured themselves, would yield in no such abject fashion. In Pest there was a realignment of political parties in 1847 and centralization upon a platform of ten points, known as the "March laws," the most important of which were: popular representation, responsible ministries, the right of public meeting, religious liberty, universal equality before the law, and the abolition of serfdom. The progressives swept into power; loudest among them was the somewhat shrill but tremendously compelling voice of a slender man with fiery eyes and unkempt hair, Louis Kossuth.

A provincial lawyer, Kossuth was not one who would be expected to lead an Empire almost to freedom. But he was clever beyond his station and years, and shortly found his way into the Diet, where his voice expressed the resentment of a nation over the treatment of the Galicians and the Ruthenians when he cried: "From the charnel house of the Vienna cabinet a pestilential air breathes upon us which dulls our nerves and paralyzes the flight of our spirit."

It was inevitable that the people should flock to the support of such a fiery leader, while in Vienna aging Emperor Ferdinand, his palsied head in a continuous shake, was impotent in the hands of Archduke Ludwig, the most hated man in Austria, and Prince Metternich, a close second. Had Ferdinand been stronger, had he been able to pursue the more kindly policies of those who had preceded him, events might have been different, but for Ludwig and Metternich there could be no compromise with the people, no yielding of any of the "Divine Rights" by which the Hapsburgs had ruled for centuries.

And so while unrest approached open rebellion in Budapest, there was the beginning of an awakening even in Vienna, the traditional stronghold of the reactionaries. Men walked the streets with lowered heads and gathered in rooms where the lights were low, while one stood outside the door to guard against the secret police of Metternich who were everywhere.

In these groups there was always sounded the muttered watchword that was soon to become the slogan of rebellion, "Metternich muss abdanken."

In revolution it is always the intelligent who start the fires, who see the need for change and are willing to give their lives for it. And all too frequently these same early leaders lose their lives at the hands of the people they finally arouse to action. In Vienna the University was the seat of culture, knowledge, and science. Here were gathered some of the greatest scholars of their time. It was natural that among this group were many hotheads, patriots who let their patriotism get ahead of their better judgment.

Semmelweis knew of this for his good friend Ferdinand von Hebra was one of the most violent of all, sometimes voicing the slogan of "Metternich muss abdanken" more loudly than was wise. Semmelweis himself was stirred by the word that came to Vienna of the reforms being carried out in Hungary, was infected by the enthusiasm of Louis Kossuth, who was nursing into flame the nationalistic fervor of a fiery race. Semmelweis would not have been the patriotic Hungarian that he was, had he remained insensitive to these events, even though preoccupied with the fight he was waging against the death that had formerly strode through the lying-in wards. But that same fight, the necessity of keeping a close watch that his prophylaxis might not be allowed to slacken by those who did not possess his own unbounded enthusiasm, and the duties of his position, now that most of the work fell upon his willing shoulders, these things certainly left him little time for talk of revolution, of political upheaval.

Sometimes Hebra reproved him for his seeming lack of interest, seeking him out in his little cell-like room near the lying-in wards. Their talk was not always on political subjects, however, for Semmelweis had much to tell Hebra of the progress of the puerperal fight, and Hebra, on his part, was full of his new classification of diseases of the skin. There was much to be weeded out of the morass of errors in which dermatology had been mired for centuries, and much work remained to be done before the appearance of the diseases in the wards could be correlated with the findings in the dissecting room and under the microscope.

Frau Hebra, too, was again pregnant, and Hebra engaged Semmelweis to attend her.

Yet such matters soon fell into abeyance before the growing fever of political affairs. Like the spark that ignites a powder keg came news of the revolution of March 1 in Paris; King Louis Philippe had fled from the Tuileries. Shortly afterwards the Hapsburgs gathered in the private apartment of Emperor Ferdinand while the crowds massed in the streets outside, their aims not yet well defined, their ardor not yet stirred by professional spellbinders to the point of flame.

Archdukes and archduchesses milled about in the royal apartment like sheep without a leader, timorous sheep, fearful of the coming of the wolf. Ludwig and Metternich were there, and the Archduke Franz Karl, who while of no importance of himself because of his childless state, although he was the heir to the throne, was important as the husband of the Archduchess Sophie, who, as Count Beust said, was "the only man in the family." Here were four horses who could never pull together.

To the Archduchess Sophie only one thing was important, the future of her son Franz Joseph, whom she worshiped and who would one day be Emperor. Intelligent as she was, she could see that in these uprisings, in the uncompromising attitude adopted by Ludwig and Metternich, and in the influence they could bring to bear upon the shaking Emperor, lay a real danger. As in Paris, royalty might be put to flight, the government taken over by the citizens themselves and the glorious inheritance of the Hapsburgs, the throne upon which she had vowed to place her son, destroyed.

Only one person in the group rallied to the support of Sophie's stand that they should make concessions. It was Archduke John, the Emperor's uncle, he who was a Hapsburg democrat and called the "White Raven." He had married an innkeeper's daughter and then forced the proud Hapsburgs to accept her as one of themselves.

John pointed out that they had been making concessions elsewhere in the Empire and that Hungary had its constitution; he pointed out also the obvious truth that they could not always keep Austria in subjection. Some of the Archdukes objected that the Austrians had been in subjection to the Hapsburgs for a dozen generations, but the Archduchess Sophie urged that they appease the angry people with concessions, else they might all go like the Duke of Bordeaux. Again the Archduke John pointed out that every dukedom in the Empire had its constitution, and that they could not keep Austria in thraldom.

The argument waxed and waned, getting nowhere. The

herd were against giving up any more of their precious position, the power they loved, the sources of income which enabled them to live off the sweat and toil of the peasants. Only these two argued on for giving in to the revolutionaries, pointing out that it was better to retain what they could of the present position and consolidate their remnants of royal privilege while they could.

Metternich took no part in the debate, but Ludwig carried it. With powerful arguments he battered down the resistance of the others until they gave in.

With the decision in the hands of Ludwig and Metternich, it was soon decided that no concessions were to be made in Vienna. No one should question the divine right of the Hapsburgs to rule Austria; no one should speak of a constitution on pain of death.

As the group were filing from the apartment, the old Emperor lifted his head and with a sudden surprising show of strength insisted: "I'll have no shooting."

When the Viennese heard of it they good-naturedly dubbed him, "I'll-have-no-shooting Ferdinand," and they cheered the poor, weak Emperor as he had never been applauded before.

Academic Vienna was in the van of the revolutionary agitation. Among the younger professors, doctors, and lawyers there were many who were loud in their indictment of the autocratic methods of Metternich and the Hapsburgs, especially when it became known that the congress of the Hapsburgs had decided that Austria should have no constitution. The foreign students left Vienna; the native students wholeheartedly joined in rebellion. All over Europe the people were rising. In Hungary, Kossuth was making his voice heard everywhere.

A true Hungarian, Semmelweis was naturally among those in academic Vienna who now rose against the government. His revolutionary sentiments, probably expressed with his usual lack of discretion, must have been a further cause of offense to Klein who stood firmly among the reactionaries.

Events marched with thunderous tread. The *Gewerbeverein*, an association of rich bourgeois, petitioned the Emperor to grant certain reforms for the better government of the nation. They were staunch men, conservatives all, and it was only the final effects of Metternich's management of Austrian affairs that forced them to take this step.

As if by signal all the other dissatisfied portions of the

empire besieged the emperor for reform in government. In vain Prince Ludwig tried to keep them from reaching the emperor, whose weakness he well knew, but the Archduchess Sophie, fighting like a she-lion for her cub, received all comers with gracious words and the assurance that everything possible would be done for them. Convinced that only Metternich stood between them and concessions from the Emperor, the mobs shuffled outside the palace and howled for his blood. Even when a proclamation granting certain reforms was made, they refused to be quieted. They now demanded virtual self-government with a constitution and responsible ministries.

And then on March 13, a company of troops under the misguided direction of the Archduke Albrecht fired upon a crowd of citizens, killing several. It was the spark that set off the tempers of the people. Barricades sprang up everywhere and there was fighting in the streets. At first the Hapsburgs were jubilant. The ill-armed citizens could have no chance against the well-drilled soldiery; the whole question of concessions would be settled finally by their tremendously more powerful arms. But disquieting news came. News that parts of the army had gone over to the side of the citizens struck fear into the hearts of the "idiot archdukes." They began to listen to Archduke John's pleading that it was not yet too late to give the people what they wished, to save them all from further bloodshed.

Ludwig was implacable and Metternich backed him up. They knew, however, that they could not long keep the news from the Emperor, especially with the Archduchess Sophie waiting to pour it all into his ears. And while they debated the crowds roared outside, "Metternich muss abdanken." The Hapsburgs swayed uncertainly, bound by their reliance upon the Chancellor in the past, fearful lest his retention would be the burden which the people would refuse absolutely to bear. Into this unsteady group came one, sent it was said by the Archduchess Sophie, who repeated aloud what the crowds were shouting in the streets, "Metternich muss abdanken."

The old Chancellor had twice spoken before the State Council that day, advising that no concession be made to a mere rabble, "a hubbub of bakers." Now he saw his royal masters wavering, and he put the question to them. He would resign only if the Imperial Family wished him to do so. The Archdukes, even Ludwig, gave their assent; the feeble Emperor, unconsulted, spoke up in agreement.

Like lightning the news spread to the crowd outside that Metternich had resigned. Everywhere was rejoicing for they were certain that only he had stood between them and the right of self-government. But they had reckoned without Ludwig. The next day it was announced that Prince Windischgrätz was appointed supreme governor of the city, Windischgrätz who was even more cruel than Ludwig, Windischgrätz who knew no law but the sword, no rights save those of his imperial masters.

Once more the fury of the people was unloosed upon the city. Barricades which had been burned gaily at the news of Metternich's going, were thrown up again. The Archdukes assembled and, following blindly in the wake of Ludwig, demanded that Windischgrätz be allowed to clear the streets. But their arguments with the old Emperor were in vain. Stoutly he stood upon his order that "there must be no shooting." Sorrowfully he threatened to abdicate if they did not obey his will. Unable to coerce him, unable to find in him a sign of the ruthlessness which had characterized former Hapsburgs and was epitomized in Ludwig of the forbidding visage, the rest of the family were forced to bow to his rule. On the morning of the fifteenth, the Emperor rode through the streets and received the cheers of the populace at his announcement that an assembly would take place to draw up a constitution which would satisfy the people. Charmed by this evidence of the love of his people, the Emperor was heard to say: "So good a people, one that love me so well, must really have this constitution for which they are hankering."

Active among the groups who clamored at the palace gates and who crouched behind the barricades with threatening looks as the soldiery passed, were numerous students who had formed themselves into an Academic Legion. They cheered the passage of the Emperor through the streets and were as loud as any in their approval of "unser konstitutioneller Kaiser." Hebra and Semmelweis were members of the Legion, as were many of their young colleagues of the General Hospital. Semmelweis could give his time freely to the cause of freedom, for there was little to keep him busy in the Lying-in Hospital now. The wards, formerly so crowded, now held few students and few patients, since the contingent from the countryside was cut off. Not that he neglected his duties: he continued to give careful supervision to the chlorine-washing as before.

One evening in that eventful spring, Semmelweis, resplendent in the uniform of the Legion, moved his antiseptic bowls to the home of the Hebras and there, late at night, he delivered the second child, tossing the baby up and again shouting gaily to the mother, "It's a boy!"

But the lull was only temporary. There was no strong man to take up the reins of this new constitutional government. Faction fought with faction, and the party of the deposed Metternich went about its way, boring subversively into the strength of the popular will. Heartened by evidence of the lack of cohesion on the part of the popular government the Archdukes grew bolder and began to plan ways to rescind the concessions which Ferdinand had made, ways to take into their own hands once more the reins of government. One of their most powerful antagonists was now no longer in the battle. Afraid that the people really meant to obtain a republic instead of a constitutional monarchy, thus depriving her son of his inheritance, Sophie grew lukewarm toward the cause she had once espoused, and withheld her aid when it might still have carried some weight.

Ferdinand, the Emperor, had been spirited away to Innsbruck where his easily swayed mind could not hear the plaints of his subjects. The nobles worked night and day to rescind the order for the constitution, but the old man was adamant. They had been certain that with the departure of the court from Vienna, the popular government would collapse; instead it grew stronger. To compensate for this they brought to the royal ears tales of anarchy and republicanism in Vienna, trying to stir him to such anger that he would rescind the decree and leave them free to turn Windischgrätz loose upon the Viennese.

In July the Reichstag met with John, the Democrat, representing the Emperor. No better choice could have been made, and had John not been sent away on another mission, all might still have gone well. On August 12th word came to Vienna that the Emperor was returning and the city went wild in welcome of their sovereign, who, though weak, had been their friend when others would have turned loose the soldiers upon them. For a short time all was well, but intrigue was soon at work again in Vienna. The Jesuits joined the old court party in stirring up strife. They found inflammable tinder in the discontent of the working classes who had been promised prosperity and had still not seen it.

And if there were not trouble enough in Vienna, strife now broke out all over the empire. There was fighting in Italy where Franz Joseph was battling Radetzky, and there was fighting in Hungary where Jellachich, ban of Croatia, had stirred up a revolt against the constitutional government of the Magyars, which Ferdinand had granted on April 12. If the fiery Kossuth were to be believed, the War Minister of Austria, Count Latour, was supplying arms and support to this revolution.

On October 3rd it became known that the Emperor had practically rescinded his order giving a constitutional government to the Magyars, for he had appointed Jellachich Viceroy of Hungary with the powers of a despot. The fighting in Hungary was now made more desperate by the knowledge that Tsar Nicholas of Russia stood ready at the borders, waiting only for an excuse for invasion. This was proof enough to the Viennese that they had been deceived by the very ruler they had lauded.

The Grenadier Regiments stationed in Vienna and long known to be in sympathy with the people were ordered to Hungary and the hated Czechs sent to take their place. Furious at the deception that was being practiced upon them, the popular government sent word to the War Minister that the Grenadiers should not leave, and when he ignored their message they captured the railway station.

This was the excuse that Count Latour had been looking for and he ordered his soldiers to attack the people. Blood flowed in the streets of Vienna and the Court Party were certain of success, but the tide soon changed. With the Grenadiers and other regiments to help them, and fighting with all the fury of people who see their freedom being taken away, the Viennese put Latour's men to flight and hung the Count himself on a lamp-post.

Certain now that there would be peace and a stable government, the people went to Schönbrunn to tell their ruler of their intentions, but he, panic-stricken at the news of Latour's fate, had fled. Next came the grave news that Prince Windischgrätz, having conquered other rebellious elements in the Empire, was marching upon Vienna to complete his task. Fired by their recent success, the citizens' army, a ragged group, ill-disciplined, ill-equipped, possessing little but the fire of enthusiasm, marched out to a rendezvous with Hungarian allies, who were even then approaching under Kossuth.

In this group marched the Academic Legion in which were

Semmelweis, Hebra, and many others of the staff and students of the Krankenhaus and the University. Studies had been forgotten since an Edict of the Emperor had closed the University on May 26. The work of the hospital was now left to the midwives and the few reactionaries who refused to be swayed by this burst of popular enthusiasm. Ill-fitted for military action, these scholars had little to recommend them for the venture upon which they were embarking, except the purity of their motives and the fire of their enthusiasm. Neither was calculated to stand up against the muskets of Prince Windischgrätz's army and when Kossuth was cut off before the rendezvous, the Viennese revolutionists were forced to scuttle back to Vienna for their own safety.

The siege of Vienna was short, and on November 1, the yellow and black flag, which the Viennese had come to regard as the emblem of despotism and tyranny, flew from the tall spire of St. Stephen's. The war was over, lives had been lost for nothing, the cause of freedom had perished for lack of a strong leader.

Back to the Krankenhaus went Semmelweis and his associates, back to their old positions, but now only upon the sufferance of the conquerors. They had secured some reforms. In April 1848 Feuchtersleben, the Professor of Psychiatry and Vice-Director of Medical and Surgical Studies had, under the pressure of the temporarily triumphant revolutionists called upon the faculty to appoint a commission which should submit to the reorganized Ministry of Education a plan for the reform of medical studies. This was done, and in consequence the medical professors were formed into a Board of Studies for the direction of the medical curriculum. A few superannuated profesors, including Wattmann the surgeon and the hospital director Schiffner, were pensioned off, but a clean sweep was impossible. Now the disappointed rebels came back to the supervision of reactionaries like Klein, whose power and influence had increased because they stood faithful to the government throughout the abortive fight for freedom.

Chapter 10

The Reception of Truth

FOR SEMMELWEIS the year 1848 was not entirely one of political and military activity. The work of spreading his doctrine went on simultaneously. In April Ferdinand von Hebra's second article appeared in the journal of the Vienna Society of Physicians. Under the title, "Continuation of the Experiences Concerning the Etiology of Epidemic Puerperal Fever in the Lying-in Hospital," he wrote:

In the December number of this Journal in 1847 there was published the highly important experience of Dr. Semmelweis, Assistant in the First Obstetric Clinic, with regard to the causation of the epidemic puerperal fever which occurs in lying-in institutions.

The experience consists (as the readers of this Journal will remember) in this, that lying-in women become ill especially when they have been examined by medical men who have had their hands rendered unclean by examinations of dead bodies, and have only washed them in the ordinary way, while no cases of illness, or very few, have occurred when the examining hands had first been washed in a watery solution of chloride of lime.

This highly important discovery, which is worthy of a place beside that of Jenner's smallpox vaccination, has not only received complete confirmation in our lying-in hospital, but assenting voices have been raised in distant foreign lands expressing belief in the correctness of the theory of Semmelweis. Among the letters received are those from Michaelis of Kiel and Tilanus of Amsterdam, from which especially we select corroborative testimony. Still in order to obtain for this discovery its full influence we would, in the most friendly manner, request all directors of lying-in hospitals to set investigations on foot and to send the results obtained to the Editor of this Journal whether they support or refute the theory. (Sinclair's translation.)

Regrettably Hebra omitted in this second article some essential information which he had included in his first editorial: he mentioned only infection of the hands from work on the cadaver and omitted all reference to infection from living organisms. The accumulation of such errors was among the most potent of the barriers to the success of Semmelweis' doctrine.

The English obstetrician, Dr. F. H. C. Routh, who had been a student in the clinic under Semmelweis, had returned to his country and there set about making converts to the doctrine. On November 28 he read before the Royal Medico-Chirurgical Society a lecture on Semmelweis' discovery; this was published in the *Transactions* of the Society in 1849, while an abstract of the communication and the ensuing discussion appeared in the *Lancet* of December 9, 1848. On January 23, 1849, Routh wrote to Semmelweis a Latin letter describing the occasion:

In the assembly of English physicians which took place last week in November (1848), I delivered a lecture in which I announced your discovery, securing the extreme honor rightly due you. I can say that my address was well received and that many of the most learned members declared that the arguments were convincing. Among these were, in particular, Webster, Copland, and Murphy, all famous physicians, who spoke extremely well of you. In the November issue of the Lancet, all of this discussion can be read.

As Routh's letter indicates, the discussion which followed his paper was in a favorable and friendly spirit, as had been the answers of Tilanus and Michaelis to the letters of Semmelweis' students. Even in the case of many of the favorable responses, however, there were misunderstandings of the Semmelweis theory, and many were the psycicians who utterly rejected the whole doctrine.

The failure of the reactionaries in Vienna to accept the Semmelweis doctrine seems to have stemmed largely from the antagonism of Klein. In other parts of the world, the trouble was largely one of misunderstanding. Semmelweis himself had discovered the cause through cadaveric infection and had at first believed that this was the only source by which it reached the mother. Later he was forced to modify his theory and it was stated in Hebra's first paper that puerperal fever was sometimes an "infection by means of putrid exudation or discharge from a living organism."

The difficulty in understanding arose largely because of a failure by most obstetricians to appreciate the importance of this second means of transmission. In Vienna there was no question that cadaveric poisoning from the dissecting room was the most potent cause of the disease, but conditions in Vienna were somewhat peculiar. It was a universal practice in Austria and many other places on the continent to make frequent post-mortem examinations. In fact, since early in the nineteenth century there had been a ministerial order requiring all physicians of Austria to perform as many autopsies as possible and to forward all interesting specimens to the pathological laboratory of the University of Vienna for further study. Since a ministerial order was almost the same as a law, the doctors rigidly observed this custom, and there can be no question that it had much to do with the renascence of Vienna as a medical center and, particularly, as the center for pathologic study in the world at that time.

The rule of post-mortem was even more rigidly observed in the Vienna General Hospital, where in accordance with a plan of studies set up as early as 1810, such an examination followed every death. In midwifery, too, it was an order that the bodies of mothers and children who died should be used for teaching, as well as the phantom. Boër had fought against this order because it violated every rule of his training and practice and his refusal to comply with it eventually led to his dismissal as professor. His successor Klein had obeyed it, with the result that one "epidemic" of puerperal fever after another occurred under his regime.

It was not generally known in England and the rest of Europe that post-mortem dissection was being practiced to such an extreme degree in Vienna and therefore when cadaveric infection was stressed by those who wrote about Semmelweis' discovery, many men assumed that his theory did not explain their own cases. It was perhaps true that they were not causing fever by carrying putrid matter from the dissecting rooms, but they were, under the complete concept, doing so by treating wounds, abscesses, erysipelas, even cases of puerperal fever itself, and then delivering normal pregnant women.

The English were especially prone to undervalue Semmelweis' theory, for they had for many years held the belief that the fever was contagious, to quote Churchill, "that it is communicated from a person suffering from childbed fever to another, who is in contact with the patient, or is in close proximity." They inclined to believe that Semmelweis was simply restating this theory in other words.

Such was not, however, the case. Semmelweis clearly dismisses the contagious theory of the disease in *Die Ætiologie:*

I do not regard childbed fever as a contagious disease, because it cannot be carried from every paitient, ill with childbed fever, to healthy ones, and because a healthy patient can contract child-bed fever from a diseased patient who is not even ill from childbed fever.

Every case of small-pox is capable of giving small-pox to a healthy person, and a healthy person can only get small-pox from a case of small-pox, but from a case of uterine carcinoma no one has yet gotten small-pox.

Such is not the case with childbed fever; if it runs its course under a form which does not produce decomposed matter, then it is not communicable to a healthy person. However, when childbed fever produces a decomposed matter, e.g. in *endometritis septica* (inflammation of the lining of the uterus), then it is certainly communicable to well persons. After death, every cadaver is a source of childbed fever for healthy patients, provided putrefaction has reached a certain stage. Moreover, childbed fever may come from diseased conditions which are certainly not childbed fever, such as gangrenous erysipelas, carcinoma uteri, etc.

Every cadaver, dead from whatever cause, is capable of causing childbed fever if the cadaver has attained the necessary degree of putrefaction.

A contagious disease is propagated by a material which can only cause the disease in question. Caries [inflammation of bone] has never yet caused small-pox. Puerperal fever is propagated by a material which is the product, not of childbed fever alone, but likewise the most heterogeneous diseases. . . .

Childbed fever, therefore is not a contagious disease, but it is a disease which it is possible to carry to a healthy person by means of a decomposed matter. There is no more relation between childbed fever and erysipelas and its sequelae, than there is with any other disease which engenders a decomposed matter; childbed fever stands in relation to erysipelas and its sequelae as to any putrefying cadaver. If the English physicians recognize, outside of puerperal fever itself, only erysipelas and its sequelae as sources of the decomposed matter which causes childbed fever, then they draw the limits too close. . . .

What could be clearer than this simple statement of truth? Had Semmelweis written these lines immediately after his discovery, instead of more than ten years later, much difficulty might have been saved. Why he did not do so will never be known. Certainly he knew better, for he himself admitted later: "I admit that it is conceivable that these objections may make a forcible impression on many individuals, and it requires enthusiasm for the affair, such as I possess, and familiarity with it, such as I have, in order to find the hidden error which is represented as truth."

In spite of misunderstandings, however, Semmelweis' theories found quicker acceptance in England and Ireland than elsewhere, perhaps because the English beliefs were so close to his own and their habits of cleanliness in obstetrics ingrained by White and his predecessors fully fifty years before.

Now, if ever, Semmelweis should have taken the opportunity to place his doctrine before the public. The statistics for the year 1848, as they were compiled, furnished striking proof. For the first time since 1840 when students had been assigned to the First Clinic and midwives to the Second, the mortality in the First had fallen below that of the Second. Semmelweis thus later described the triumph of his prophylaxis:

In 1846, when the chlorine-washings were not yet in use, there died 459 puerperae out of 4010 in the First Clinic, or 11.4%. In the Second Division during 1846, out of 3754 there died 105 or 2.7%. In 1847, when about the middle of May the chlorine-washings were introduced, there had died in the First Division 176 out of 3490 puerperae, or 5.0%. In the Second Division 32 died out of 3306 or 0.9%. In 1848, when the chlorine-washings were used assiduously throughout the year, 45 puerperae died out of 3556, or 1.27%. In the Second Division during this year, 43 died out of the 3219 delivered, or 1.33%.

I have assumed that the cadaveric material adhering to the examining hand of the accoucheur is the cause of the greater mortality in the First Obstetrical Clinic; I have eliminated this factor by the introduction of the chlorine-washings. The result was, that the mortality in the First Clinic was confined within the limits of that in the Second, as the above cited figures show. The conclusion, therefore, that the cadaveric particles adhering to the hand had in reality caused the preponderant mortality in the First Clinic, was also a correct one.

Since the chlorine washings were brought into use with such striking results, there was not the slightest change made in the conditions in the First Clinic, to which could be ascribed a share in the diminution of the mortality.

Despite this growing mass of proof for his doctrine, Semmelweis stubbornly refused to publish. Such evident truths, he apparently thought, must make their own way in the world. His friends, despairing of him, took various ways to further his cause, as Hebra had already done.

In January, 1849, Skoda presented the case of the Semmelweis doctrine before the Board of Studies of the Vienna Medical School. Since the former director of medical studies had wholly ignored the accomplishment of Semmelweis,

Skoda stated, it was the duty of the Vienna medical faculty to undertake an investigation of this important innovation, evolved within their own institution. He advocated the appointment of a faculty commission to undertake various tasks. They should construct a statistical table showing the correlation between puerperal-fever mortality in the past and the extent to which students and assistants had occupied themselves in dissection. They should investigate the alleged low mortality among cases of street-birth. They should ascertain whether the puerperal-fever mortality was always low in institutions where the possibility of cadaveric infection was excluded. They should test the new theory by experiments on animals.

Skoda's proposals exploded like a bomb-shell in the faculty meeting. Klein was furious. He opposed the investigation fundamentally, certain that the proposed statistical report on conditions in the Lying-in Hospital could contribute nothing whatever to the explanation of puerperal fever, for he steadfastly credited the increase and decrease in the disease to the vagaries of uncontrollable epidemic influences. Moreover, he took the very suggestion of investigation as a personal insult and was bittter at such interference by his colleagues in the administration of his clinic. The ophthalmologist, Rosas, recently appointed acting Vice-Director of Medical and Surgical Studies, sprang to his defense, describing Skoda's proposal as a slander on Klein. Skoda had many backers in the faculty group, however; his recommendations were adopted by a strong majority. Of the eleven professors voting, only three were in the negative: Klein, Rosas, and Reimann.

The joyful news of this success was communicated to Semmelweis. His high hopes were soon dashed, however, for Klein at once addressed to the Ministry of Education a protest against the resolution of his colleagues. And Rosas, whose function it was to place before the ministry the minutes of the faculty board, made full use of the opportunity to calumniate Skoda before the higher authorities. Very soon Skoda found himself subjected to a furious counter-attack by clerical and medical groups on the score of his "materialistic opinions." In February the ministry's decision came. The right of the medical faculty to force an investigation upon Klein was denied; he himself was to conduct such investigations on puerperal fever as he saw fit, preferably at a time when the disease was flourishing and could be better observed.

The commission, already appointed, was dissolved. Stupidity had stifled free inquiry. The reactionaries had won. Political power was securely theirs, and the democratic faction in the University had no recourse against them. Semmelweis was hardly helped by the fact that his native country was still in revolt against Austrian rule. Hungarians had little place or influence in Vienna in 1849.

On February 23, Dr. Karl Haller, who bore the imposing title, "Chief Physician and Provisional Director of the Imperial and Royal General Hospital in Vienna, and the institutions connected with it" (the Imperial and Royal Lying-in, the Psychiatric, and the Foundling Hospital), read to the Vienna Society of Physicians a statement on the Semmelweis prophylaxis and its results. He was preparing his report for the year 1848, and was so deeply impressed by the statistics of the First Obstetrical Clinic as compared with the record of the Lying-in Hospital for the past twelve years that he took up the defense of Semmelweis. After discussing these statistics and praising Semmelweis' achievement, he proposed that Semmelweis be asked to speak before the society. The proposal was adopted, but Semmelweis, with his usual reluctance, neglected this opportunity for proclaiming his doctrine just as he had neglected all other chances which had come his way.

Haller's full report, printed later in the year, made a definite bid for recognition of Semmelweis' work by the Ministry of Health, and must have infuriated Klein. It may be quoted at some length, not only because it shows that Semmelweis' work was fully appreciated by some of his colleagues in Vienna, but also because it shows that both Semmelweis and his friends realized the importance of the prophylaxis to surgery. There can be no doubt that Semmelweis was a pioneer in antiseptic surgery, at least fifteen years before the great achievements of Lister in that field. Haller wrote:

The mortality rate in the two large free divisions of the lying-in hospital is almost the same, and must be called satisfactory from every viewpoint.

For years there has been, however, a serious difference. The First Obstetrical Clinic, under the direction of Professor Klein, and to which all male students are exclusively assigned, had a shockingly large mortality, compared with that of Professor Bartsch's School, where all midwives receive their instruction.

The reasons for this highly disturbing phenomenon were never established with certainty. The great merit for their discovery belongs to the Emeritus Assistant of the First Obstetrical Clinic, Dr.

Semmelweis. Actuated by the suspicion that the numerous cases of illness and deaths among the puerperae could probably be attributed for the most part to the introduction of a cadaveric poison during vaginal examinations by students and obstetricians also busy in the dissecting room, and that this transfer of cadaveric poison was not prevented with complete certainty by the then customary washing with soapy water, in May 1847, with the consent of Professor Klein, he caused every physician and student in the clinic to wash their hands carefully with the chloride of lime solution before every initial examination of a parturient or puerpera, and this washing was repeated after every examination of a puerpera ill even to the slightest degree. The consequent performance of this measure had surprising results, even in the first month.

The number of deaths decreased promptly in 1847 with almost the same number of births to 283, and sank from 11.4% to 5.04% in the course of the year 1848, but when these washings were carried out persistently and methodically throughout all the months of the year, the mortality rate equalled that of the second Obstetrical Clinic; it was perhaps even still about 0.1% more favorable.

Since the decreased invalidism and mortality among the mothers was also a life saving measure for the newborn, their mortality decreased to a remarkable extent.

Convincing proof for the correctness of these conclusions can be obtained by the reader from a comparative glance at the . . . tables, in which the births and deaths of the three divisions of the lying-in hospital for the last ten years are arranged together, and in addition, it must be noted that the mortality rate is only approximately correct, since during the prevalence of puerperal epidemics at the First Obstetrical Clinic for sanitary and humane considerations, a not inconsiderable number of sick puerperae were transferred from the lying-in hospital to different divisions of the general hospital and are omitted from these reports as dying there.

The significance of this practical knowledge for the obstetrical institution, for hospitals in general and *especially for the surgical wards* [italics author's] is so immeasurable that it appears worthy of the most earnest consideration of all men of science, and is certain of suitable acknowledgment by the high state government.

As von Waldheim points out, the story of the reception of the Semmelweis discovery is a strange one indeed. The first proponents of the new doctrine were Hebra, the dermatologist, and Skoda, the Professor of Internal Medicine. The first to recognize its significance for surgery was the physician Haller. Klein, the obstetrician, maintained a contemptuous silence, and the surgeons, Schuh and Dumreicher, able men

though they were, openly ridiculed Haller as a fanciful en-
thusiast and utterly rejected his suggestion that Semmelweis
had made a valuable contribution to their field. Had one of
them but had ears to hear with, the history of antiseptic surgery would have begun in Vienna in 1849.

Such was the state of affairs in March of 1849 when Semmelweis applied for a two-year extension of his position as
Assistant in Midwifery. He had staunch friends and supporters, but many influences were ranged against him. The de-
ciding factor was the hatred of Klein.

On March 20, 1849, Semmelweis ceased to be Assistant in
the First Division of the Lying-in Hospital. His application
for reappointment had been denied. Karl Braun, who had no
better recommendation than that he had invented a decapita-
tion hook for delivering babies who had died within their
mothers' bodies, took his place. There was bitter irony in the
fact that Semmelweis, who had brought life where formerly
there had been death, should yield his place to a man versed
only in handling the dead.

Ill-advisedly, Semmelweis protested and appealed against
Klein's decision, to no avail. When he realized the fruitless-
ness of the proceeding he petitioned for appointment as Privatdozent in Midwifery, a position comparing somewhat with
that of a clinical professor in modern medical schools. It was
certainly a better position and more commensurate with his
ability than the one which he had lost.

Meanwhile, at Skoda's suggestion, Semmelweis undertook
to prove his conclusions, based hitherto on strictly clinical observations, by experiments on animals.

For his helper in these experiments, Semmelweis chose
Rokitansky's assistant, Dr. Lautner, who was relieved from
other duties for the task. In March, 1848, a period of patient
work began for them both. At first they used brushes to contaminate with infectious material the uteri of female rabbits
who had just cast their litters. Later they used only a syringe,
to remove the possibility of any effect from the brush. Some
of the animals were infected with blood from cadavers who
had died of various diseases. Some were inoculated with pus
removed from the pleural cavity, the space around the lungs.
Some were inoculated with pus from various abscesses; still
others with the milky fluid of peritonitis and of puerperal
fever.

From March 22 to August 20 nine experiments were carried out, of which all but two resulted in the deaths of the animals from pyemia. After summing up these experiments years later in *Die Ætiologie* Semmelweis added a remark which showed that he had never once doubted the validity of his theory: "It is scarcely necessary to mention, that the changes found in the cadavers of the rabbits are the same as are found in human cadavers as a result of puerperal diseases and in general following pyemia."

The experiments came to an abrupt end, and Semmelweis to a chill realization of the lengths to which his opponents would go, when Lautner was arrested and examined on the ground that he had taken part in the 1848 revolution. The charge was a mere pretext and he was soon released, but he had seen enough of Austria. He made his way to Egypt, obtained a post as court physician, and died soon afterwards of fever.

For Semmelweis there followed a long period of idle waiting while the Ministry of Health considered his application. It cannot have been a happy time. Bad news came regularly from Hungary. Kossuth's declaration of independence, April 24, 1849, had brought division in the ranks of the revolutionaries, many of whom wished only to secure their constitutional rights under the Empire. In May, eighty thousand Russian troops had entered Hungary, on the invitation of Emperor Francis Joseph, who had succeeded the feeble Ferdinand in the preceding December. The Hungarians fought on bravely, but the combined force of Russians, Austrians, and Croats overpowered them at last. On August 13 the Hungarian army under Görgei surrendered to the Russians at Világos. Kossuth and five thousand of his men escaped to Turkey, where the Porte gave them sanctuary. Hungary was once again defenseless in the hands of despotic rulers, who took a bloody vengeance. The property of all rebels was confiscated; all the old rights of the people were abolished; patriots were executed. On the sixth of October Count Batthyani was shot as a rebel in Budapest, and the same day saw the execution of thirteen Hungarian generals. Of Semmelweis' four brothers, all but one had been active as rebels and now became refugees.

All through these weary months Semmelweis waited for a response to his application for the Privatdozent license. His patience began to wear thin, and his sense of injustice grew ever keener. All of his reforms in the Lying-in Hospital were being neglected. While there was some attempt at prophylaxis even under his successor Braun, there was no close supervision of the technique. The puerperal fever began to increase once more; many bodies of mothers appeared on the tables of the post-mortem room where in Semmelweis' time there had been but few. In vain he stormed again Klein and his followers as murderers. His indignation served only to strengthen their antagonism against him and delay action upon his application.

Their antagonism showed itself also in more direct manifestations. Criticisms of his behavior in the administration of the First Clinic were spread through the Medical School to the detriment of his reputation. And when, under Skoda's urging, he undertook to increase his statistical records on the state of affairs in the Lying-in Hospital before the introduction of his prophylaxis, he was flatly denied access to the records. It seems apparent that Klein and the reactionaries were hoping that he would leave Vienna in despair, for they hindered his progress in every possible way.

In their machinations, however, they failed to reckon with one potent force—Skoda. Having interested himself in the career of Semmelweis the clinician was not one to be discouraged by a single defeat. As Rokitansky once said of him, Skoda was a beacon for the learned, a model for the aspiring, and a rock for the disheartened. He never forgot his own conflict with the forces of convention, when, dismissed to limbo, he might have remained there but for the help of powerful friends; he now used his own power without stint to help those who deserved his aid.

For two years Skoda, like Semmelweis' other friends, had tried vainly to persuade Semmelweis to publish his theory and its proofs in complete and authoritative form. He had not done so. Now Skoda determined to perform this function himself. He borrowed from Semmelweis all of his notes and records in the fall of 1849, and from these prepared an article which he read at a meeting of the Imperial Academy of Sciences on October 18.

This address won for Semmelweis immediate election to membership in the Academy of Sciences, and on Skoda's motion the Academy offered to Semmelweis and to Brücke, the Professor of Physiology, funds to enable them to continue animal experimentation on puerperal fever. Brücke readily expressed his willingness to collaborate in these investigations, out of a sincere desire to further the progress of so beneficent a discovery.

Skoda's paper, which was published not only in the *Transactions* of the Academy of Sciences but also by Hebra in the journal of the Society of Physicians, was in many respects an excellent presentation of the puerperal picture. He surveyed the facts upon which Semmelweis had based his discovery and showed how those facts annihilated the epidemic theory of the fever. After a remarkably clear exposition of the pathology of the disease, he discussed the use of the chlorine prophylaxis and gave statistics proving the value of this preventive measure. He briefly described previous attempts to publicize the discovery. He reviewed the animal experiments carried on by Semmelweis and Lautner and recommended further research in this direction.

Unhappily Skoda fell into two errors. The first, an error of omission, was that he emphasized the cadaver as a source of infection and made no reference to the possibility of infection from the discharges of living organisms. The second, an error in tact, was a reference to the Prague obstetrical clinic. Skoda alluded to the letter he had written to Nadherny in 1847 when he was convinced that the great frequency of puerperal fever in Prague resulted from the same cause as that in Vienna. He had urged, he now said, that the chlorine-washings be introduced in Prague. From the sequel he concluded that either the believers in the epidemic theory had gotten the upper hand at Prague or else the chlorine-washings had been conducted with reprehensible carelessness. Such a reference, in an address by so distinguished a figure as Skoda, could hardly be ignored by the Prague obstetricians, who at once began to busy their pens in rebuttal.

Meanwhile Brücke gave further evidence of his sincere interest in Semmelweis by addressing to his friend Professor Joseph Schmidt of the Charité hospital in Berlin a letter on the doctrine. Unfortunately, as a natural result of Skoda's lecture, he mentioned only cadaveric infection. Schmidt's reply, courteous and measured, said only that he accepted the possibility of cadaveric infection. He expanded on the subject in the next volume of the *Annals* of the Charité, referring favorably to Semmelweis and declaring that he would certainly require precautions in his clinic against the possibility of cadaveric infection, but he stated plainly that while the cadaver might be one of the sources of infection in puerperal fever, it was certainly not the only source. It is indeed a pity that Semmelweis himself did not make his doctrine available in a comprehensive form to such sympathetic and potentially helpful readers as Schmidt. When he at length published *Die Ætiologie* he devoted several pages to this incident, expressing himself with an acerbity which Schmidt certainly did not deserve.

Still waiting with growing impatience for some answer to his application for the appointment as Privatdozent, Semmelweis must have been alternately excited and depressed by these developments with regard to the spread of his doctrine. Another letter came from the devoted Routh in December: he reported from London that the Semmelweis doctrine was rapidly gaining in the public esteem and was recognized by all medical societies. "For great is the truth," he concluded, "and it will prevail." Another former student, Wieger, had returned to Strasbourg with a firm resolution to introduce the discovery of Semmelweis in France. In 1849 he wrote an article on the subject and submitted it to the *Union Médicale*. There it was published, to be sure, but under the heading, "Doubtful Anecdotes," among other bits of questionable humor about the Vienna Medical School. Wieger subsequently published his article in pamphlet form, but since he was young and unknown and since his chief at Strasbourg opposed the Semmelweis doctrine, the gallant effort was ineffectual.

In February 1850, Semmelweis again applied for recognition as Privatdozent, having received no answer at all to his first application. Again he waited. And now the replies excited by Skoda's address began to appear. The Professor of Obstetrics at Prague had virtually retired and left most of his duties to his aggressive assistant, Scanzoni. The latter had published in 1846 an article on childbed fever in which he declared the essential element in the disease to be fibrinous crasis of the blood which, under certain cosmic-telluric influences, rose to a high degree and caused the fever. Now, in 1850, Scanzoni wrote as much to defend his pet theory, so flatly opposed to that of Semmelweis, as to defend the Prague clinic against Skoda's accusations.

The major points of his vindication may be reviewed briefly. He rejected, first of all, Skoda's summary of the facts which led to Semmelweis' discovery; this material, he said, contained nothing new, for it was universally known that more puerperal fever occurred in lying-in hospitals than outside them. This choice bit of fallacious argument neatly evaded the major point at issue, for, as we have seen, the proof of the Semmelweis doctrine was precisely this body of statistics and observations which Scanzoni so coolly shoved aside. He then went on to Skoda's attack on the Prague obstetricians, saying that Skoda had made much capital of the fact that numerous epidemics occurred at Prague arising apparently from the same source as those at Vienna—cadaveric infection resulting from extensive occupation of students and faculty in the pathology laboratory. Why then, Scanzoni asked, had Semmelweis and Skoda never directly communicated the former's so-called discovery to the directors of the Prague clinic? Scanzoni and his colleagues had heard of it but only indirectly; they did not understand what Skoda meant in saying that he had informed them of the value of chlorine-washing but that they had neglected this prophylactic measure.

Skoda's slander was unjustified, Scanzoni went to to say, for as soon as the Prague obstetricians heard rumors of the Vienna successes with chlorine-washing, they had introduced the practice with great care and attention. They had continued it through a month and a half, reducing the number of their visits to the pathology laboratory at the same time. No decrease in the number of puerperal fever cases was observed. They gave up the washings, and shortly afterward the cosmic-telluric influence passed away and their epidemic disappeared.

Many words follow, all to much the same point: refutation of Skoda and Semmelweis by evasion of their arguments: defense of the Prague clinic and of the theory of epidemic influence. Misleading statistics, erroneous because they excluded from among puerperal fever cases two most dangerous forms of the disease, were presented to show that the Prague mortality was lower than that in the Vienna clinic during Semmelweis' term of office. The whole is a sickening document, of interest only in showing with what energy and ingeunity men can conduct themselves in the fight against truth.

Shortly after writing his reply Scanzoni became Privatdozent at Prague and left his part in the controversy temporarily to his successor in the assistantship, Seyfert. The latter soon put his contribution on record. It is hardly worth attention, being largely a recasting of the arguments of Scanzoni with some additional statistics indicating the utter inefficacy of chlorine-washing at Prague, the whole expressed in phrases of smug self-satisfaction.

There is no doubt that Semmelweis read these articles with care and with growing indignation. His doctrine had been ignored and misunderstood before; now he found it misrepresented, with deliberate falsifications brought up to disprove it.

There was little to cheer him in those months of almost hopeless waiting for his appointment. Some encouragement came from a publication by Bednar, Chief Physician of the Foundling Hospital. In a monograph on a disease which he called sepsis of the blood in the newborn, Bednar stated that cases of the disease had grown rare thanks to the discovery by Semmelweis, who by preventing puerperal fever had saved the babies as well as the mothers.

Such testimony was a help, but it could not silence in Semmelweis' mind the taunts of Scanzoni and Seyfert. Moved by those attacks as he had never been by the urging of Skoda and his friends, he broke his long silence. Wieger, discouraged by the reception of his article in France, had begged Semmelweis himself to send a communication to the French Academy of Sciences. Semmelweis now did so, but he received no acknowledgment. He arranged also to deliver an address on his findings before the Vienna Society of Physicians, of which body he had been elected a member on June 6, 1849.

His first lecture took place on May 15, 1850. It consisted of a clear and complete statement of the whole history of his discovery. He stated his theme plainly: "Puerperal fever is . . . as little a contagious disease as it is a specific disease in itself; it develops in this way, that an animal organic material which has become putrid, whether originating within a diseased living organism or from a cadaver, taken into the blood mass of a puerpera, produces a puerperal, pyemic blood-dissolution, whence result the well known exudations and metastases."

He thus declared, as had Hebra in his first article, that the disease can be caused by material from living bodies as well as from dead ones. He also mentioned for the first time the possibility of infection from unclean utensils. And yet the criticism was leveled against him time and again by sundry terriers who always yapped on the trail of such great ones, that his theory could not be true, because he attributed puerperal fever to cadaveric dissection, yet it occurred where there was no dissection. The reason for this implacable opposition will probably never be completely clear. Certainly his opponents were not all reactionaries, for Scanzoni contributed a technique of forceps delivery in posterior presentations which has been standard for almost a hundred years.

At the next meeting of the Society of Physicians on June 18, Semmelweis spoke again. This time he devoted his attention to refuting the arguments of Scanzoni and other opponents of his doctrine. His honest indignation carried him away and he expended energy and labor in compiling careful replies to men whom he might better have disregarded. Among these was a Viennese physician, Dr. Zipfel, who, having first congratulated Semmelweis on his discovery, later attacked him furiously, perhaps under Klein's instigation, and still later claimed the whole discovery for himself and an English writer, Ferguson. Semmelweis' address on this occasion, wasted effort for the most part, contained one point of great importance: in reply to Seyfert he suggested that his prophylactic measures would be of value in gynecological survey.

Semmelweis made an excellent impression upon the Vienna Society of Physicians, which was strengthened at the July meeting. In the debate a Dr. Lumpe made some adverse comments, suggesting that the doctrine was not sufficiently proven, but concluding that "we must wash and wait." Chiari, Helm, Arneth, and Rokitansky spoke warmly on Semmelweis' behalf.

The series of lectures could be regarded as a marked step forward for the doctrine. But again Semmelweis made a mistake. There was ample reason, now that he had discussed his theory before one of the leading medical organizations in the world, for him to publish at least a monograph upon his work. Unfortunately he trusted to the publication of the minutes of the meeting to give his work the publicity it deserved and demanded. Hebra had already said much the same thing in his first article and there had been little reaction. Semmelweis should have profited by that knowledge and found a wider sphere for his own work. But for some reason he again refused to write, and though his spoken message had carried a tremendous appeal to the men who heard it, it could not long survive in their minds the repeated attacks of his enemies, who displayed no objection to seeing themselves in print.

Semmelweis was soon to be disheartened by the entrance of a new and powerful opponent on the scene. He had hoped much from Kiwisch of Würzburg, who, in response to Skoda's letter, had visited Vienna in 1848 and 1849. Now Kiwisch published his comment on the Semmelweis discovery, a comment which, coming from an obstetrician of such authority and experience, was bound to carry weight. The first blow came with Kiwisch's denial that Semmelweis' theory of infection by decomposed animal matter was a new one. It had been suggested long ago, he said, but had never been seriously adopted because its adherents had never been able to produce sufficient proof. Then, after a slight bow to Semmelweis for his perseverance, Kiwisch went on to betray the fact that he had confused the Semmelweis theory with the contagion theory of the English. Kiwisch admitted that he had practiced the prophylactic measures of Semmelweis very slightly, if at all, then went on to credit all appearances of puerperal fever in his own clinic to epidemic influences.

Under Kiwisch's direction the mortality at Würzburg had been high, rising to 26% in one year. How a man could put aside the memory of so many dead mothers and blandly repudiate, without a fair trial, a plan for avoiding such mortality is hard indeed to conceive.

After such an attack as this Semmelweis cannot have seriously minded the next, which came from Dr. Lumpe of Vienna, who had once been an assistant under Klein. Lumpe's essay, the sequel of his inconsequential remarks before the Society of Physicians in July, was a wonderful assembly of obscure statements, false logic, and prejudice, all with the purpose of disparaging Semmelweis' theory. Next came a more effectual but equally illogical article by Scanzoni, now categorically denying some of the statements on which Semmelweis' proof rested. These repeated buffetings might have shaken the most patient of men into publishing retorts, but Semmelweis had resumed his silence.

At last on October 10, 1850, the answer to the application came, appointing Ignaz Philipp Semmelweis as Privatdozent for Theoretic Midwifery, "with restriction to the use of the phantom for teaching."

To Semmelweis the anatomist, the scientist, the tireless searcher after truth, this was the crowning insult. It made him little more than an attendant upon the artificial mother —the phantom—to which his demonstrations were to be limited. The rules required that instruction on the cadaver as well as the phantom be included in the obstetrical course. With his restricted appointment, therefore, Semmelweis could not even give certificates to his students. With no facilities for dissection, with no way to enforce his doctrine once more in the wards of the Lying-in Hospital, he was to become a mere puppet. The news was confirmed by the catalogue for the fall semester which listed "Lectures on obstetrics with practical demonstrations on the phantom five times a week by Dozent Ignaz Semmelweis."

Klein and his followers had succeeded; they had struck

him in his most vulnerable spot, his professional pride. They made him realize, moreover, that he could not hope for success in the face of the political and social influence they wielded so unscrupulously against him. There is little wonder, then, that Semmelweis fled five days later from Vienna to Budapest. He was leaving the hated city behind him, the city where he had so nearly attained success, but where he had also known bitter heartbreak.

It is hard to condemn Semmelweis for his flight, but it is harder to see how he could leave without even saying goodbye to the loyal friends who had stood by him through the fight: to Skoda who had done so much to help him with pen and speech; to Rokitansky who had acted almost as a father to him in his scientific researches; to his good friend Hebra whose sons he had delivered; to Chiari who had been his instructor in midwifery and a loyal friend through the years; to all his other many friends in the Krankenhaus.

There must have been some grim faces at the next meeting of the Academy of Sciences. Brücke rose to announce that he was returning his share of the experiment funds to the Society, since Semmelweis had left Vienna. He reported that he and Semmelweis had attempted some experiments but found their results ambiguous. Brücke, like Semmelweis, had arrived at the conclusion that not animal experimentation but rather the compilation of clinical statistics was the preferable method of proving the Semmelweis doctrine.

Undoubtedly the sudden flight from Vienna was the crowning mistake in the life of Semmelweis, a life in which there were all too many tragic mistakes. For had he stayed things might well have been different. There was room for a good professor of midwifery in Vienna at the time; many of the older men had been called to other universities, and others were soon to go. Semmelweis might have accepted his limited appointment and bided his time: Klein and Rosas were old and could not hold their power long. Or if he could not wait, and certainly he had had enough of that, he could have appealed the appointment and shouted from the housetops the scandal that hung over the Lying-in Hospital. He knew and could have proved the bald fact that because of stupidity and hate women still died like flies, when a way had been shown, which even the simplest could understand, to prevent every death.

If he had taken either of these courses he would soon have learned that there had been trickery in his appointment. Later investigation showed that under the act of the Minister of Health Ignaz Philipp Semmelweis had been appointed Privat-dozent, "with practice on the phantom and the cadaver." Maliciously or accidentally someone had changed the wording of his appointment. The news came too late, for he had already flown and alienated the friendship of those who might have regained for him all he had lost.

The world lost more that day when Semmelweis left Vienna than he did, unhappy though he was. For had he remained, the truth must surely have spread more rapidly, both for obstetrics and for surgery. And who knows but that he might have received full credit for his great discovery while he lived, and might have seen countless mothers and children saved who died because the doctors of Vienna were too blinded by ignorance and prejudice to see the light of the "puerperal sun which first shone in Vienna in 1847."

Chapter 11

The Second Trial, St. Rochus

THE BUDAPEST to which Semmelweis returned in October, 1850, was a far different city from the one he had known in his youth. The heel of the conqueror was heavy upon it. For nine months after the surrender at Világos in August, 1849, Count Haynau had administered the penalties of martial law, trampling out the last vestiges of revolutionary spirit. The city was still under close supervision. Public gatherings whether political or scientific, were permitted only with the stipulation that police agents attend. Austrian spies were everywhere, contributing to the disorganization of society by creating an atmosphere of distrust. In 1851 an Imperial Council for Hungary was to be appointed, and for years thereafter Hungary was held under by despotic rule, her government offices filled by foreign bureaucrats, all her people's old rights denied to them.

To this stagnant atmosphere Semmelweis returned. Of his family there remained only a married sister and his oldest brother, Paul, a minister of religion. Paul had changed his last name to the Hungarian form, Szemerényi. Three other brothers, a grocer, a farmer, and a soldier, were still in exile.

The city was as beautiful as ever, for the resistance to Windischgrätz had been short-lived and the city had not been razed. Over the Danube stretched the graceful cables of the new suspension bridge which English engineers had completed the year before, replacing the old stone-pillared bridge over which he had walked as a boy on his journeys to and from the University.

Other old landmarks were the same; the University with its ivy-covered buildings where few students went nowadays; the graceful spire of St. Stephan's, in whose shade he had played as a child; the fishing boats lying beside the wharves bobbing slowly on the brown waters of the Danube, with their short masts and high carved prows, looking just as they had when he'd watched them as a boy; the merchants' stalls along the quay, each shaded from the sun and protected from the rain by its large white umbrella.

Yet there was a difference in Budapest. It lay in the faces of the people whom he met on the streets. An old woman trudged along, her face lined, her eyes red from weeping for her son who had fallen while fighting against the Russians for Kossuth and freedom. And the serious mien of a scientist told of liberty restrained, of opinions which he dared not utter, of the lack of good heartening talk with his fellow scientists and teachers which is the heart of the academic existence. The tavernkeepers bemoaned the fact that people no longer possessed the price of a glass of beer and a sandwich of cheese and dark bread, and a gypsy, fiddle strings ragged and worn, cheeks gaunt with hunger, found few patrons to listen to his wild music and throw coins upon the floor for eager fingers to clutch. The spirit of the people, if not crushed, was for a while at least oppressed by a burden which seemed beyond bearing.

There was one ray of brightness in all this gloom. In Budapest Semmelweis resumed his friendship with Ludwig von Markusovszky. It had been a long time since he had seen his impetuous friend, for Ludwig had returned to Budapest to practice after leaving Vienna in 1846, and Semmelweis' work had been too absorbing these past years to allow even a short visit to his home city. Into his friend's sympathetic ear he could pour the story of his failure in Vienna. And if Markusovszky realized how Semmelweis had doomed his own beloved doctrine by failing to fight for it with every power he possessed, he did not further depress his friend by pointing out the truth.

Scientific life, Semmelweis learned from Markusovszky had degenerated to a low level. Von Balassa, professor of surgery, had been imprisoned for a time, and many of the teachers at the medical school and university were dead or were in disfavor with the Austrians, a fate almost equally bad. The only medical journal published in Hungary, *Orvosi tàr* (Medical Magazine) had ceased to exist in 1848, and its editor, Paul Bugát, had been deposed and placed under police surveillance. All meetings of men of science had been forbidden, except in the presence of a police officer, and no statement of any kind could be made which might be construed by the Imperial Council as treason. Even so, this half-life was better than the living death of the Russian occupation.

Renewing his friendship with Markusovszky brought Semmelweis face to face with the reality of his own position. With his small funds almost gone, he must soon decide what to do about the future, no matter how deep his depression. He had received little pay as an Assistant in Vienna, and the savings of his family had been wiped out by the revolution.

The logical avenue toward self-sufficiency lay in entering the practice of obstetrics in Budapest, but he could not hope to succeed even there unless he were able to obtain some sort of a hospital appointment which would aid in making his ability known. The best course would be to obtain a connection with the university and the medical school. Of von Balassa's good will, he could feel certain, for the old man had been a friend of the family of many years' standing. But von Balassa himself was not in favor with the new regime.

The outlook, on many counts, was not good and Semmelweis, in his depressed spirits, recognized this. In the old days he would have thrust himself into the fray, actively working for the position to which he was entitled by reason of his ability and fame as a former Assistant at Vienna, that of Privatdozent in Midwifery. With this position to recommend him, he could then quickly develop an excellent practice among the upper classes and the Hungarian aristocracy.

But if he expected immediate recognition, he reckoned without Hofrat Birly who had headed the Department of Obstetrics for many years. To his amazement Semmelweis found that his work in prophylaxis of childbed fever through chlorine-washings was practically unknown in Budapest. This must have been another crushing blow to his belief that his beloved doctrine must inevitably make its way by virtue of its own importance as a life-saving measure. Birly had a theory of his own, and a dearly beloved one, on the subject of puerperal fever. He held that the fatal infection resulted from too little purgation. His treatment, relied on in the Medical School, was to purge every mother thoroughly after delivery, on the naive assumption that thereby the body would be rid of the humors which caused the disease.

Almost before Semmelweis had an opportunity to decide on his course in Budapest, the answer was thrust in his way. He describes the event in *Die Ætiologie:*

I spent one of my first evenings in Pest in the company of a large number of physicians. Because of my presence, the discussion turned upon childbed fever, and it was urged in vindication of the objections against my theory, that in the lying-in division of the St. Rochus Hospital in Pest, even then as all through the year, a furious epidemic of puerperal fever was raging, although there were no examinations made by students, whose hands were polluted by decomposed animal-organic matter, because the obstetrical department in the St. Rochus Hospital was not used for teaching.

The next morning, in order to see the situation with my own eyes, I went to this lying-in hospital and found a puerpera dead just then of puerperal fever, the body not yet removed, another moribund and four others seriously ill with puerperal fever, the other patients present were not puerperae, but suffering from other diseases. Thus was established the actuality of an unfavorable state of health among the puerperae, not in contradiction to, but in harmonious corroboration of my theory of the origin of puerperal fever, because closer inquiries showed that the obstetrical division was not a separate department, but was assigned to the surgical division and the chief accoucheur [obstetrician] was at the same time chief surgeon and coroner. In addition because of lack of prosectors, the autopsies must be done by the physicians of the respective departments.

The chief was accustomed to make rounds in the surgical division, then in the obstetrical department; while no examinations were made by students, whose hands were defiled by decomposed animal-organic matter, in the obstetrical division of the St. Rochus Hospital, yet the chief and the physicians assigned to him made examinations after they had previously contaminated their hands with decomposed organic matter during their visits to the surgical department.

We have previously shown that the greater mortality in the First Clinic in contrast with the Second was due to the cadaveric material, which clings to the hands of the examiner. We have pointed out that in October, 1847, ichorous particles from a discharging medullary carcinoma of the uterus had caused childbed fever. We have shown that in November, 1847, ichorous particles from an odorous carious knee had caused childbed fever.

In the obstetrical division of the St. Rochus Hospital, the exciting factor for childbed fever was the different decomposed animal-organic substances which are found so abundantly in a surgical department.

Here certainly we see evidence that Semmelweis appreciated the importance of antisepsis in surgery.

The situation at St. Rochus was ready made for a demonstration of the effectiveness of the doctrine of Semmelweis, and with a surge of his old spirit he leaped into the battle once again. He addressed a petition to the authorities of Budapest to allow him to take over, without recompense, the direction of the obstetrical department of St. Rochus Hospital.

Early in 1851 the *Vienna Medical Weekly* carried a notice to the effect that the well-known Dr. Semmelweis had been appointed Privatdozent in the University of Pest under Professor Birly to lecture on practical obstetrics, for which use two rooms in the St. Rochus Hospital had been assigned to him. And on May 20, 1851, his petition granted, Semmelweis became honorary senior physician, without pay, in the Obstetrics Division of St. Rochus Hospital, Budapest. The battle against maternal deaths after a brief respite, was joined once more, to continue until his death.

St. Rochus Hospital belonged to the municipality of Pest and was fairly large, even for European hospitals, which tended to be of the pattern of the great Allgemeine Krankenhaus in Vienna. It had six hundred beds. Three medical and two surgical chiefs formed the medical faculty of St. Rochus. The department of obstetrics was a section of surgery, as Semmelweis had learned on his first visit to the wards.

Nor was the obstetrical clinic at St. Rochus in constant use, as would have been in keeping with the presence at its head of an obstetrician of Semmelweis' caliber. During ten months of the year, while classes were being held at the University, only those mothers who were prematurely seized with labor pains while being treated in the hospital for other reasons were delivered in St. Rochus. All others went regularly to the University where they were used by Hofrat Birly in his teaching. Only during the months of August and September, when the University was in recess, were large numbers of mothers delivered at St. Rochus. Hitherto, puerperal fever had raged unchecked through the wards during this period.

The arrangements of the department were none too satisfactory. The space used by Semmelweis was on two floors, consisting of one labor room and two lying-in rooms with six windows opening out, appropriately enough before Semmelweis' coming, upon the morgue. However, a street on the ground floor allowed the smell of the deadhouse to dissipate itself without rising in too great a concentration to the windows of the lying-in division.

Such were the meager facilities available to Semmelweis at St. Rochus, in charge of the department of obstetrics. What a demotion it was from the great First Clinic at the Allgemeine Krankenhaus. But it was a place to work, and work was what he needed most of all in his present state of depression.

He busied himself immediately during the slack period, arranging matters so that with the coming of patients to the hospital during the summer vacation at the medical school, a place would be prepared for them. A ward was set aside for the use of obstetrical patients, with the plan that during the winter it would be used for gynecological cases, a speciality in which Semmelweis was highly skilled by virtue of his long years of study of the female body and its diseases. Only by arranging for such isolation, could he be certain that infected surgical cases did not come into contact in any way with freshly delivered mothers. By controlling this obvious source of puerperal infection he hoped to avoid the annual epidemics of puerperal fever at St. Rochus, which were already a scandal in the city. And with the obstetrical work isolated in one section, he could more effectively put his prophylaxis into effect.

The change from the slovenly habits common to surgeons all over the world at that day to the rigorous antisepsis of the Semmelweis doctrine was not easily accomplished, although he watched the technique as closely as ever he had the students in Vienna. Even so, an assistant once performed an autopsy on a patient who had died of gangrene and went directly to the delivery room; the result, a death from puerperal fever.

As he had in Vienna, Semmelweis set up rigid procedures and insisted on their being followed absolutely, fanning the animosity which seemed to rise against him everywhere he went because of the "Lehre" which was his life blood. In spite of these minor misadventures, he was accomplishing a miracle never before seen in Budapest, and only once before in Vienna. The facts of the record, as presented in *Die Ætiologie,* were an incontrovertible proof that he was right:

In the vacation months of the school year 1850-51, there occurred 121 births in the obstetrical department of St. Rochus Hospital; for 1851-2, 189 births; for 1852-3, 142 births; for 1853-4, 156 births; for 1854-5, 199 births, and for 1855-6, 126 births.

Thus during these vacation periods, there occurred 933 births, with 24 deaths, and actually from childbed fever, 8, or 0.85%. The other 16 puerperae died from the different diseases, for which they were being treated during pregnancy and were transferred to the obstetrical department at the onset of labor.

Thus there died in the obstetrical department of St. Rochus Hospital less than 1% of the puerperae from childbed fever during the six years, where previously childbed fever had exacted so many victims.

In the face of such evidence, a mortality so sharply in contrast with the terrible epidemics which had hitherto existed in St. Rochus, and also far below the record of the university clinic itself, it would seem that the truth of Semmelweis' claims must have been immediately apparent even to the most obtuse. But the same story was repeated again. The evidence had no effect upon hidebound Hofrat Birly, who went on serenely teaching that puerperal fever was a disturbance of the body due to a neglect of the "prima viae," to be rectified by means of purgation, with as little result as had been achieved by the thousands of methods of treatment advocated before the coming of Semmelweis.

In another field, however, Semmelweis achieved a measure of success. His fame as an accoucheur had spread through Budapest and he soon began to build up a satisfactory practice among the better class of Hungarians. Along with this success, and undoubtedly partly accounting for it, came a resurgence of his interest in social life. He had always been a gregarious boy, laughing and singing much of the time. But with the coming of puberty a change had occurred in him, a tendency toward introspection which at times almost became morbid. His years of close work in the laboratory and in the wards of the Krankenhaus had done little to counteract this tendency and his subsequent disappointment at the hands of Professor Klein intensified it. Now, perhaps in reaction, he turned in another direction. He learned to swim and to ride, and in March and July, 1851, he succeeded in fracturing his right arm twice in his efforts to master these sports.

Another tendency was manifesting itself more noticably now. This was a trend toward eccentricity, a lack of thoughtfulness in his relations with others. He had never been known to be particularly considerate of the feelings of those with whom he came in contact, especially if he felt that they were doing something in the wrong way. This accounted for much of the animosity he had stirred up while in Vienna. Fired by a purpose or an idea, he sometimes behaved oddly, as in the case of one of the Budapest nobility, a countess whom he examined for a suspected malignant tumor of the pelvis. His diagnosis was cancer, but during the day he began to brood upon his findings, with the result that in the evening he became uncertain that he was right. With typical impetuousness he rushed to the house of the patient, demanded to be admitted unceremoniously made his way to her bedroom, and repeated the examination, confirming his suspicion that he had been wrong and that what he had thought a malignant condition was actually a simple pelvic tumor. The lady's gratitude for the good news was apparently submerged in indignation at the affront to her dignity.

Meanwhile Semmelweis kept up his attempts to find a suitable teaching position, for he was not entirely happy in obstetrical practice in Budapest and was cramped by the limited facilities of St. Rochus Hospital.

In September, 1851, Lange, Professor of the Midwives' Clinic at Prague was called to Heidelberg, and his post at Prague was vacant. When Semmelweis heard of the vacancy he immediately prepared for a trip to Prague to press his claims for the position, for here was the chance he had been looking for, an opportunity to put his methods into effect in a clinic where he was in complete authority as Professor. In that way he could prove to the world that his prophylaxis was everything that he claimed. He seems to have forgotten that the controversy of 1850, the echoes of which still sounded, had made his name something less than popular and welcome in the obstetrical circles of Prague.

Traveling to Prague he found his old Vienna friends Chiari and Arneth on the same train, bound on the same mission. They had a grand reunion, for they had been fond of each other during the Vienna years. Both Chiari and Arneth had been vigorous advocates of the Semmelweis doctrine: Chiari had spoken up for Semmelweis in the very teeth of Klein, his father-in-law, at the meeting of the Vienna Society of Physicians; Arneth had carried the news of the chlorine prophylaxis to Paris and Edinburgh during the spring of this very year. He could now give Semmelweis a firsthand account of the trip. Unhappily he could not report unqualified success. In Paris he had addressed the Academy of Medicine in January 1851, but though the Academy had appointed a committee to investigate the matter, no report was forthcoming, and Arneth's inquiries met with discourtesy. The *Gazette des Hôpitaux* for January 9, 1851, had, however, carried a notice to the effect that the Academy of Medicine had pronounced itself firmly opposed to the Semmelweis doctrine.

From France Arneth had gone to England, and thence to Scotland where, in May 1851, he delivered a lecture before the Medico-Chirurgical Society of Edinburgh; the lecture had been published in the *Monthly Journal of Medical Science* in June. Arneth had capably presented in this paper all the most significant points of the Semmelweis doctrine, and it had been favorably received.

It was possibly on this occasion also that Semmelweis learned of his endorsement by the great British obstetrician, Sir James Y. Simpson, who had so discourteously answered Arneth's letter in 1847. In November 1850, Simpson had published an article pointing out the identity of puerperal and surgical fever:

In childbed fever and in surgical fever, the fever is not the cause of the accompanying inflammations, but the fever as well as the inflammations are the result of the common cause, namely the original corruption of the blood. But what causes the corruption of the blood must be answered in a later era with a more developed pathologic anatomy, histology, and chemistry.

In support of this statement Simpson had adduced the favorable results secured by Semmelweis in preventing puerperal fever by taking measures to exclude the unknown factor which caused "the corruption of the blood." Thus Simpson retracted his error and conceded the value of the Semmelweis prophylaxis.

The journey to Prague was a memorable one for Semmelweis, and in his joy at renewing old friendships he probably found that the time passed too quickly. The three had no occasion to quarrel because of the position at Prague; all were rejected, on the ground, they were told, that none of them spoke the Czech language. Under Dr. Johann Steng, the successful candidate, the puerperal-fever mortality in the Midwives' School at Prague soon rose to 13%!

Semmelweis still failed to publish the results of his studies, although evidence was daily mounting in St. Rochus Hospital of the efficiency of his methods of antisepsis in preventing puerperal fever. And while he went on working miracles there, puerperal fever raged at the University Clinic in the same city, where aging Hofrat Birly still held forth as Professor of Midwifery, as adamant as ever against admitting the ideas of Semmelweis to his clinic.

Chapter 12

The Third Trial, Pest

ADAMANT AGAINST new ideas though he was, Professor Birly was not adamant against death. Early in 1855 he died quite suddenly, leaving the chair in Obstetrics at the Medical School of the University of Pest vacant. Almost immediately an article sent from Pest appeared in the *Wiener Medicinische Wochenschrift*. The name of the author is not given but the tone of the article sounds like Markusovszky, who fully appreciated the value of publicity, since he was soon to be editor of a new Hungarian medical journal, *Orvosi Hetilap*. The article outlined in no uncertain terms the situation created by the death of Birly.

The late Professor of Midwifery (Birly) was an honourable man whose sudden death has caused the deepest sympathy and regret in the widest social circles. He was a man of learning, and possessed all the endowments required in a teacher, and yet it would not be going too far if we expressed the opinion that long before his death he had ceased to be a professor of midwifery according to the present day requirements of medical science, teaching the manifold methods of diagnosis and the new ideas with regard to pathology so urgently demanded in every good school of medicine. . . . It is no indiscretion to mention that both professional and public opinion supports the appointment of Dr. Semmelweis to the vacant professorship. . . . Dr. Semmelweis, when assistant in the Lying-In Hospital of Vienna acquired, owing to his lectures and his courses of practical and operative obstetrics, a reputation extending far beyond the boundaries of the Monarchy; and he has attained already a great position in medical practice in our city. . . . If the recently revived scheme of erecting a new lying-in hospital is carried out, and proper facilities for teaching are afforded in it, then will be opened up to our energetic obstetric specialist a wide field of activity and a new era in obstetric science will commence in our Father Land. (Sinclair's translation.)

Semmelweis was well known in Budapest by now and his reputation as an accoucheur and a gynecologist was of the highest. In addition he had been careful not to stir up political fires since his return, and it was considered very patriotic of him to have returned to Budapest in the time of her mourning. Nor was there any rival for the position whose attainments even remotely equaled his own.

With all these recommendations it is not surprising that in July, 1855, Ignaz Philipp Semmelweis was appointed to the position of Professor of Theoretical and Practical Midwifery in the University of Pest. This time there were no strings attached.

The tide of disaster, it seemed, had turned, and his departure from Vienna five years before appeared, partly at least, to have been vindicated. A new period in his life began, the brightest page in all the dark chapters.

In accepting the position of Professor of Midwifery in the Pest medical school, Semmelweis was materially improving his professional position, but it is doubtful if he was bettering at all the conditions under which he must work. The obstetrical clinic at the University was, if possible, in even worse condition than that at St. Rochus, where he had been able to make such amazing progress. The state of the clinic is best described in an anonymous article appearing in the Vienna medical weekly, entitled, "The Medical School at Pest," No. V, which Semmelweis reprinted in *Die Ætiologie:*

The (obstetrical) clinic is situated on the second floor, and indeed in the furthermost part to the rear of the whole building, so that the poor women in labor must not only travel considerable distances from one part or the other of the city but are compelled to drag themselves up two flights of stairs and through a long corridor, so that it happens that births on the stairs are not a rarity. This injudicious location of the clinic at a considerable distance from the entrance of the building is even more harmful in a lying-in hospital, because, on account of the limited space, only such women are admitted whose labors have begun or are imminent, and not in the last two months of pregnancy as in Vienna. Not only does the location of the clinic in the sense indicated above leave much to be desired, but the windows on the one side open on the dead-house, while the others are directly over the dissecting room. As if that were not enough, there are to be found in one wall of the actual sick-ward about three, well-drawing chimney flues of the chemical laboratory on the first floor directly underneath the obstetrical clinic, which in the middle of the summer turn the wall into a veritable giant oven. If one does not believe this, let him place his hand on the wall; I know for a fact, that he will not do it a second time and will take my word for it in the future.

The clinic consists of five rooms, of which three have one window, one two windows, and lastly a corner room with three windows. Of those with one window, there is one so small there is only room enough for the nurse. Accordingly there remain only four little rooms for the puerperae. The delivery room, as already stated in a previous letter, has only one window and three beds, one of which stands against the window. One should now picture a busy clinic, attended this semester by 93 pupil-midwives and 27 medical or surgical students, with the thermometer at 26°R in the shade—and if one has a sufficiently lively imagination, let him imagine finally the troubles of the operating Professor under such conditions, or the tenfold distress of the patients being operated upon. Here also, as in the wall with the chimneys, was recently offered to every optimist a rich opportunity for a penetrating *argumentum ad hominem*. There lay on the diagonally placed bed, a truly pitiable creature; instructor, assistant, and a dense throng of pupil midwives and medical students stand around it; even in the third room beyond they are closely packed head to head, able only to hear the patient's screams, without being able to see; heat, that was rather more capable of forcing one out of the world than of attracting one into it; the sweat stood out in beads on the forehead of the professor, as the version (an obstetrical operation) was complete, and just as he was in the act of introducing the first blade of the forceps, he came so near to an actual faint, that he was compelled to give over to his assistant the instrument that he was inserting and to remove himself from the unbearable atmosphere of the clinic. It is truly remarkable, and in any case, speaks wonders for the rational and scrupulous care of the puerperae, that puerperal diseases in the last year in spite of all these difficulties have rather decreased than increased. But what would one do with the sick patients, if indeed that were not the case, since, besides the 3 labor-beds, there are only 23 beds available, i.e. in the one-window rooms three, in the two-window room with the artificial tropical climate eight, and in the corner-room twelve. If indeed one cannot imagine that the course of the puerperium

in Africa is not a more favorable one, we can convince him of it
in a more gentle fashion, viz. with a simple exercise in numbers.
During the course of the school year, there were nearly 600 deliveries, which was possible only because the puerperae as a rule
left the institution with their babies the ninth day; if puerperal
fever raged here as in the lying-in hospital in Vienna, then scarcely
the number of 100 births would be attained.

But this, one might say, is a fine quality in the obstetrical
clinic, and we would be the last to deny it; but the material for
instruction, as is apparent, is in a bad way; of what use are 600
deliveries, if one is scarcely able to see a dozen of them! As is
well known, a good two-thirds of these occur during the night,
but are lost as far as instruction is concerned, for there is scarcely
room for lodging the students of pupil midwives at night. Conse-
quently, only the two students on watch have opportunity for
learning and even this only at the expense of their health, because
they must pass the night in an overcrowded sick-ward; again by
day, as previously indicated, one must endure a few thumps indeed, if he wishes to penetrate into the small labor-room. Nothing
is more dangerous for the student than the idea, that his effort is
in vain; if this is once firmly established in his mind, then follows
indifference or disgust in place of the original zeal, and even the
scant opportunity is neglected, which may be offered here and
there to one desirous of learning.

As for the lectures, the situation is no better. Because there is
no proper lecture room for this department, the Professor of
Obstetrics is compelled to hold forth, when and where he has the
opportunity, in winter on the ground-floor in the acologic lecture-
room and in the summer in the surgical lecture-room. That the
lecture room should not be overly occupied at seven in the morning and mostly by candle-light in the winter-time would not be a
great misfortune, because it is a matter of common knowledge
that the so-called theoretic obstetrics in the third year of the medical course is not worth much and should soon give way entirely
to a more rational teaching plan; but that the exceedingly important practical demonstrations on the phantom should be given,
due to the lack of the aforementioned "When and Where," in the
corridor between windows and doors, stairs and wash-kitchen, before a class of 130 men and women—that is as flagrant an abuse
as is possible only in an exceptional school. I make bold to ask,
has one the right to condemn the country surgeon, who, not so
long ago, did not recognize a uterine rupture, and altogether un-
knowingly severed a piece of gut? Was it possible, even with the
best of intentions during his course of study, to obtain sufficient
knowledge of this the most difficult of all the practical branches?
Or is it not much more surprising, that such a tragic *"Quiproquo"*
happens so seldom, that is to say, that in spite of such obstetrical
teaching so many infants are born alive?

Operative courses are an indispensable aid for instruction in obstetrics, they carry the beginners as a rule much further along the road to courage and skill, than do similar courses in surgery; but what is to be done about this part of the instruction in a teaching institution, where there is usually a lack of cadavers?

Finally, there is not the slightest opportunity to study gynecology, a disadvantage which also prevails elsewhere indeed in obstetrical clinics, but a substitute for it is to be found in the gynecological section of the same building. Up to a short time ago, and moreover for six whole years, the Professor of Obstetrics has conducted in the St. Rochus Hospital a small department for diseases of women, entirely without remuneration; the opportunity was thus given him to initiate one or another diligent students into this important subject, and thereby do an incalculable amount of good for thousands; this has also, against his will, now come to an end. Such tragic blunders as putting a piece of intestine into the pocket, do not happen every day, but daily the curet is used for plethora, instead of the ligation of a polyp; and every day *Rheum* with *Aloes* is prescribed, instead of notice being taken of the excoriation present; in reality the young physician is admitted to practice with an ignorance of the diseases of women, which makes one actually afraid for the continued existence of the more lovely half of humankind, which is moreover the greater.

This valuable contemporary account not only gives us a glimpse of Semmelweis at work but also places vividly before us the grave difficulties which he faced in the Obstetrical Clinic of Pest. The conditions there were probably not very much worse than those in almost any other lying-in hospital in Europe at that time. Better arrangements existed in the Allgemeine Krankenhaus in Vienna, but even there puerperal fever was still rampant. It is hardly to be expected that results in other clinics were any better, except in the few isolated spots where the Semmelweis doctrine of antisepsis was being rigidly practiced. In these, as in Budapest, the "puerperal sun which shone in Vienna in 1847" was able to illumine even the darkness of ignorance and inadequate facilities.

This state of affairs must have discouraged a less strong-minded man than Semmelweis, but to him it was merely another chance to demonstrate the truth of his beloved *Lehre*. Upon entering on his duties in October, 1855, he threw himself into the work with whole-souled vigor, even buying linen out of his own meagerly filled pockets when the economies of a purse-shy government did not provide the necessary supplies.

Nor did the difficulties stop with the physical arrangements of the clinic. The staff resented the intrusion of a stranger into Professor Birly's place. Some of them had undoubtedly expected promotion at the death of the professor. They resented, too, the trouble that all the hand-washing caused them, the minor irritation to the skin and the much major irritation to tempers held none too well in check. In a hundred little ways, as the students and midwives had done in Vienna, nurses, midwives, and even doctors tried to circumvent him in his methods. But Semmelweis had always been a ruthless task-master as far as the technique of prophylaxis was concerned. Time and time again he sent students back to the washing bowls, ignoring their black looks and muttered imprecations. Time and again he excoriated nurses who were negligent, pouring out upon them the bitter irony of which he could be such an accomplished master. He was irascible at times, quick to fly into a rage, but just as quick to recover when things were done according to his orders.

Working under such difficulties, Semmelweis accomplished what must be regarded as a miracle. Five hundred and fourteen patients passed though the midwifery clinic of the University in the first year of his tenure. Of them, only two died of puerperal fever, a mortality of 0.39%. No hospital in the world could have boasted of such a record, certainly no hospital in Europe could even approach it at that time; even five years later, Achilles Rosa noted in the Hospital of the University of Jena that, "no lying-in woman left that institution alive. All died from puerperal fever." It is little wonder that Semmelweis was jubilant over the results that first year, that he was willing to discount as nothing all the difficulties, all the long hours spent drilling the facts of midwifery and particularly of childbed fever into students and midwives, nurses and staff.

Yet, though he now had to his credit two successful demonstrations of his prophylaxis in Budapest, Semmelweis still abstained from giving his doctrine clear and authoritative publication. And in the absence of such a declaration from him, those who opposed or ignored his theory had a clear field.

Thus Kiwisch, who had removed to Prague, had again delivered, in 1851, his professional ukase against Semmelweis in a volume of lectures on the special pathology and therapy of female disorders. His comments on puerperal fever in this volume showed no advance over his former stand. It is clear

that Kiwisch was still under a misconception as to the full
extent of the Semmelweis doctrine: he still believed it had
only to do with cadaveric infection. And cadaveric infection,
he said coolly, could not have much to do with the matter. He
had himself continued to go from the pathology laboratory
to the delivery rooms, but had found no grounds for sup-
posing that this practice had any particular effect on the recurring epidemics of puerperal fever in his clinic. Then a
slight retraction: in institutions where there was a possibility
of infection by decomposed animal matter, it would be fool-
hardy not to take such precautions as the English and Semmelweis advocated. Kiwisch seems almost to have regarded
chlorine-washing and other antiseptic measures as fetishes, to
be employed—with no great thoroughness, one gathers—to
avert the evil eye of epidemic influences.

Kiwisch died in 1851 and Chiari succeeded him at Prague.
Chiari was a loyal adherent of the Semmelweis doctrine, and
it seems strange that he did not take advantage of his new
position to begin public demonstration and defense of his
friend's theory. On June 27, 1851, he had spoken briefly before the Vienna Society of Physicians on a case of puerperal
fever; the autopsy had shown no uterine inflammation. He
had made no reference to the bearings of this case on the
Semmelweis theory, and enemies took this article as an indication that Chiari had turned against Semmelweis in publishing a case which could not be explained in accordance with
the Semmelweis doctrine. This was certainly not the case: it
is possible that Chiari kept silent out of deference to his
father-in-law, Klein, or to spare the Vienna friends of Semmelweis, still angry at the abrupt departure of the preceding
October. Chiari's silence continued during his Prague years
(1851-1854), but he employed the Semmelweis methods at
Prague, as will be seen.

In von Waldheim's biography of Semmelweis the general
attitude toward the new prophylaxis in the early fifties is ex-
cellently illustrated by references to various textbooks on obstetrics appearing during that period. In 1851 Rosshirt of
Erlangen published a *Lehrbuch der Geburtschilfe* which
naively described puerperal fever as the growth of inflammation resulting from the rapid stretching of the peritoneum
in delivery. In 1852 Tormay of Budapest, Semmelweis' own
city, published a handbook for midwives containing no reference whatever to the need for cleanliness and disinfection.

In 1853 the old opponent, Scanzoni, now professor at

Würzburg, put out the third volume of his obstetrical textbook. His description of puerperal fever presented it as almost a different disease from that which Semmelweis described by the name, for he further developed his earlier practice of describing many of the principal types of puerperal fever—endometritis and the like—as separate disease entities. He again attributed the causation of the disease to epidemic influences and boasted that he had himself been the first to oppose the now rejected Semmelweis doctrine. The second edition of this textbook, published in the same year, showed no change with regard to the words on Semmelweis, and in a *Compendium of Obstetrics* which appeared in 1854, Scanzoni had nothing to say of cleanliness and disinfection.

Such was the case, also, in the third edition of Lumpe's *Compendium of Practical Obstetrics,* of the same year. Although present in Vienna during the years which saw the first test of the Semmelweis prophylaxis and although partially converted to the doctrine at that time, Lumpe had now wholly abandoned his tentative stand of 1850: he had ceased to "wash and wait."

These and many other instances of the neglect or rejection of his doctrine came one by one to the notice of Semmelweis, but he steadily ignored them, as far, that is, as any public rebuttal was concerned. His own experiments with the prophylaxis were triumphantly successful, and he trusted that the truth would make its own way. Unfortunately when it did, and when the directors of lying-in hospitals tried, apparently not very conscientiously, to apply the chlorine prophylaxis in their hospitals, they too often reported unsatisfactory results. A mortality of 3.3% by Retzius of Stockholm, 15% by Faye of Christiania! These reports could only provide more ammunition for the enemies of the doctrine.

In 1853, moreover, an event occurred which gave those who were enemies of Semmelweis himself rather than of his doctrine a means of declaring themselves on the side of the truth while opposed to its discoverer. In that year Arneth published an account of his study tour in France and Great Britain, describing the state of obstetrics and gynecology in those countries. Arneth began his tour as a disciple of Semmelweis, devotedly preaching the gospel. In London and Dublin hospitals he acquired a new enthusiasm. Here was order, cleanliness, ventilation, to a degree never conceived of in Vienna. His book refers repeatedly to these undoubtedly excellent features of the British hospitals he had seen, as well as to the care with which British obstetricians isolated puerperal-fever cases and disinfected contaminated areas. In so doing, Arneth unwittingly supplied the personal enemies of Semmelweis with a way out. They could practice prophylactic measures, yet give the credit to the British rather than to a bumptious Hungarian whom they despised. Hence the entrance on the scene of a new and powerful antagonist, Karl Braun.

On succeeding Semmelweis as Assistant in the First Clinic on March 20, 1849, Braun had carried on the chlorine prophylaxis, rather than risk by its discontinuation an outcry from Semmelweis and his friends. But he had conducted the practice half-heartedly, describing his predecessor's theory as humbug, and his subordinates had been quick to take advantage of the laxity of his supervision. Within that very March a score of women died of puerperal fever, and Braun's record was poor throughout his assistantship, which lasted until the fall of 1853.

In July, 1850, in commenting on the Semmelweis doctrine before the Vienna Society of Physicians Lumpe had cited the month of March, 1849, as that showing the maximum of mortality during the practice of the chlorine prophylaxis. Semmelweis justifiably but tactlessly answered in rebuttal that the mortality of that month was proof only that the prophylaxis had been inadequately administered in the days after his departure from the clinic. He thus directly accused Braun of negligence, and the accusation could have but one effect: Semmelweis had made another bitter enemy.

In 1853, the year when Arneth's book was published, Braun went to the Professorship of the Midwives' School at Alle Laste, Trent, leaving his Vienna assistantship to his brother Gustav Braun who succeeded in losing four hundred patients by puerperal fever in the course of 1854. At Trent Karl Braun completed the greater part of his work on a textbook of clinical obstetrics and gynecology in which he was collaborating with Chiari, then in Prague, and Spaeth, Professor of Obstetrics in the Joseph's Academy of Vienna. The theoretical part of the book, the whole of which was published in 1855, was Braun's and included his first attack on Semmelweis. He presented a lengthy discourse on the etiology of puerperal fever, listing no less than thirty possible causes of the disease. These included the state of pregnancy itself, the long duration of the birth process, the plethora common to pregnant women, emotional influences, a disproportion in the "vegetation" of mother and foetus, undernourishment, high room temperature, and inadequate ventilation. If read to a group of physicians today this solemn list would provoke only amusement. In its day it probably seemed the height of wisdom, for it covered all the possibilities. Even cadaveric infection was included, as the twenty-eighth of the thirty items.

Braun proceeded to discuss his list thoroughly. Arriving at No. 28, he began his assault on Semmelweis, repeating the same old error by restricting the Semmelweis doctrine to cadaveric infection. He reviewed briefly and inaccurately the evidence presented by Semmelweis, then went on to refer to the opponents of the theory. Among the opponents he included Chiari. Then he took the points of Semmelweis' evidence and disparaged each in terms of his own experience. Thus, he cited against Semmelweis' Vienna demonstration of the success of the prophylaxis, his own sorry Vienna record. He had used the recommended prophylaxis, yet the puerperal fever epidemics had occurred nevertheless. He questioned the value of Semmelweis' animal experiments, described by Skoda; could not the animals have developed pyemia from injury to their gential organs by the means of experimentation? And so on.

Yet with all these arguments against Semmelweis, culminating in a measured statement that cadaveric infection had little, if any, importance as a cause of puerperal fever, and in a denial that chlorine-washing was effectual in removing cadaveric particles, Braun actually subscribed to the Semmelweis doctrine, for he described it as an act of presumption to permit students to work with puerperae when their hands retained any hint of cadaveric odor. In addition, as an adherent of British principles, he strongly emphasized the great importance of the position, ventilation, and cleanliness of the lying-in hospital. This was published in a year when Semmelweis was proving the value of his prophylaxis for the second time in Budapest under unfavorable hospital conditions which would have driven Braun to despair.

In the light of our present knowledge Braun's arguments against Semmelweis are ridiculous and ineffectual; certainly the falsity of his statement of Semmelweis' case is immediately evident. But in his time his semblance of experience and thoroughness carried great weight. He stepped at once into the first rank of Semmelweis' opponents.

Braun's inclusion of Chiari among the opponents of the

Semmelweis doctrine, while of little significance in his argument, was undoubtedly a painful surprise to Semmelweis. He thought himself betrayed by his old friend. He seems not to have learned until later that Chiari had died of cholera early in 1855 and had probably not read Braun's statement before his death. Chiari's acceptance of the Semmelweis doctrine had never wavered, as was made clear by an article on his experiences in Prague which was published after his death in the *Journal* of the Vienna Society of Physicians on February 19, 1855. He described how at Prague two puerperal-fever epidemics were produced by putrid discharges from the genitals of patients during labor, and told how he had carried on the Semmelweis prophylaxis in all its details, with a few added precautions of his own devising.

In April 1856, Professor Klein in Vienna died. Who knows how many hours Semmelweis must have lain awake, dreaming of the triumph that could be his if the position were given to him, of the triumphant return he would make to the Krankenhaus, his theories vindicated, the seal of approval put upon his life's work. How he must have longed for the company of the scientists who had been his friends, the physicians who were making the Vienna Medical School the greatest of its day. Who knows the eager anticipation he must have felt as the day of the appointment approached, the fearful agony of doubt and worry that must have tortured him at the same time? And he could have accomplished much for the vast number of women who went every year through the portals of the great hospital to the Lying-in Division, many still to find their ultimate destination upon the cold white table of Rokitansky's laboratory.

But his great ambition was not to be realized. On July 19 the directing board of the Vienna Hospital published its list of nominees; two weeks later the faculty's recommendations were made public. The name of Karl Braun headed both lists, that of Semmelweis appeared on neither. His omission was the final answer of his Vienna colleagues to his abrupt and foolish departure in 1850.

Perhaps in an effort to bring his work back to the memories of those in Vienna, perhaps as a reply to Braun's systematic attack, Semmelweis permitted his Assistant, Dr. Fleischer, to contribute a report of the school year 1855-56 to the *Vienna Medical Weekly*. In the report, the use of the Semmelweis prophylaxis was described and to it was attributed the low mortality reported. The paper was published in the Vienna journal. The following editorial comment was added: "We thought that this theory of Chlorine disinfection had died out long ago; the experience and the statistical evidence of most of the lying-in institutions protest against the opinions expressed in this article: it would be well that our readers should not allow themselves to be misled by this theory at the present time."

As a monument to human stupidity, this editorial comment left nothing to be desired!

Vienna's rejection of Semmelweis was to be made complete on December 5 when the appointment of Karl Braun became an accomplished fact.

Disappointed in his hopes for a triumphant return to Vienna, Semmelweis had still his undenied success in Budapest to comfort him. He found little time to indulge in depression, for, in the school year 1856-57, puerperal fever broke out once again in his clinic. In that year sixteen women died, where the year before there had been but two fatalities.

This was a challenge which could not be ignored, if everything Semmelweis had fought for was not to be swept away. While his doctrine had spread but slowly, this bad news, like all tidings of ill fortune, would be widely bruited about as a refutation of his discovery. He tackled the problem with characteristic vigor. His teaching duties had been so arduous, the hours required of him as a Professor and Regent of the University so long, that much of the burden of supervising the routine operation of the clinic had been shifted to the younger assistants, men whom he hoped would go out one day to spread the truth thoughout Hungary and Europe. It was too much to expect that they would devote to such an apparently routine matter as maintaining cleanliness the energy which Semmelweis had himself always given to it.

When he began to give his personal attention to the problem of this new appearance of the disease he had spent his professional life fighting, one curious fact asserted itself at once. In ordinary cases where infection was carried to women before or at the time of delivery by putrid matter on the hands of the accoucheur or midwife, the appearance of the disease in the mother was almost always accompanied by an almost identical pyemia in the child, causing death in both at about the same rate. But here the children were spared. Mothers went on dying, but their children lived, untouched as a rule by infection. To Semmelweis' alert mind, this could

year, with a far lower mortality, this condition was immediately reported by the Professor, and appeal was made for a greater provision of bed-linen, which was immediately granted to the extent that a supply of several hundred sheets over the requirements remain for disposal. Likewise the supplies of beds and their equipment, and body-linen were furnished to the entire amount requested, during the vacation months, to such an extent that the high cost of providing them did not escape the notice of the Honorable Ministry for Culture and Education.

Therefore the Imperial and Royal Professor shares also the conviction with the rest of the personnel who are familiar with the clinic, that it is not due to lack of linen, even less to the regular delivery on the part of the laundress, but that the inattentive and unregulated management of the change of linen carries the blame for the increased number of cases of illness and death.

To this wholly unjustified charge, Semmelweis replied with a calmness unusual for him; perhaps he had learned by now the futility of thrusting evidence beneath the Director's aristocratic nose:

It is indeed my conviction, as well as that of the other persons, who are familiar with the clinic, that the increased mortality observed in the beginning of the school year 1857-58 at the obstetrical clinic of this place should not be ascribed to the lack of linen, nor to the irregular delivery of the same on the part of the laundress, but that the inattentive and unregulated management of the change of linen should bear the blame for the increased sickness and deaths. But this inattentive and unregulated management of the change of linen is not the fault of the chief midwife, but of the nurse, N. N., who was discharged for that reason.

In the school year 1856-57, 31 puerperae died, 16 of them from childbed fever on account of the want of linen and the irregular delivery of the same on the part of the laundress.

In the school year 1857-58, 24 puerperae died, 18 of them from childbed fever on account of inattentive and unsupervised change of linen.

There were never more than two deaths in one day; if it is said that in the school year 1856-57 there was a much smaller mortality and that at the beginning of the school year 1857-58 the mortality was so great that even up to ten puerperae died in one day, this statement is not in accord with the truth.

Since the bed-clothes soiled with the blood of dead parturients were never furnished to new arrivals, then those sheets, soiled with blood and lochial discharge, and returned from the laundry as washed clean, must be referred to, the same sheets, which I personally had the honor to display, with the information, that these sheets had caused childbed fever in my clinic.

The memory of that foul emanation of the year before must still have been repugnant to von Tandler, and certainly this direct refutation of his charges by Semmelweis did little to improve relations between them. Nothing was done to relieve the unbelievably bad conditions in the obstetrical clinic, although Semmelweis pointed out again and again the inadequacy of the facilities with which he had to work. But with the stopping of the epidemic due to the careless nurse, his prophylaxis was again able to produce the results in preventing fever and in saving mothers and babies which had characterized it wherever it had been used.

Semmelweis must have realized that he himself was partly to blame for the impediments by which he was so frequently blocked in his fight against puerperal fever. Still no authoritative publication, and more than ten years had elapsed since his first discovery. He had made no move to answer all the lies and errors heaped up by his opponents. Without an outlet, how the bitterness must have grown within him—against Scanzoni, Seyfert, Braun, and the whole host. How his mind must have boiled with plans for proving the shortsightedness and the dishonesty of his enemies. Yet he had kept his silence, confining his outbursts to the small circle of his friends and colleagues.

Meanwhile his doctrine had continued to be the subject of publicity, almost always adverse or erroneous.

In 1855, Oliver Wendell Holmes in the United States, reprinted his essay on puerperal fever under the title *Puerperal Fever as a Private Pestilence*. In the introduction he demolished at some length the arguments which had met the publication of the original paper, pointing out what English accoucheurs such as Charles White had observed more than fifty years before. Following the original essay appears "Additional References and Cases." Here he refers to several papers describing the Semmelweis doctrine as follows:

Routh's paper in Proc. of Royal Med. Chir. Soc., Am. Jour. Med. Sc., April, 1849, also in B. and F. Med. Chir. Review, April 1850.

Skoda on the Causes of Puerperal Fever. (Peritonitis in rabbits, from inoculation with different morbid secretions.) Am. Jour. Med. Sc., October 1850.

Arneth.—Paper read before the National Academy of Medicine. Annales d'Hygiene, Tome LXV. 2ᵉ Partie. (Means of Disinfection proposed by M. Semmeliveis [Semmelweis]. Lotions of chloride of lime and use of nail-brush before admission to lying-in wards.

Alleged sudden and great decrease of mortality from puerperal fever. Cause of disease attributed to inoculation with cadaveric matters.) See also Routh's paper, mentioned above.

Thousands of miles from Vienna and Budapest we see the unfortunate idea persisting that Semmelweis attributed childbed fever only to infection transmitted from the cadaver. Holmes' second publication apparently had little influence on the spread of the doctrine of chemical prophylaxis in the United States. Unfortunately the controversy stirred up by his original essay—in which he predicted from theoretical considerations the very things which Semmelweis proved at the bedside, in the delivery room, at the post-mortem table, and in the experimental laboratory—was so great, and the caliber of his opposition, like that of Semmelweis, so considerable, that much of the truth was undoubtedly lost in the volcano of words which ensued.

As we have seen, Arneth's efforts to introduce the Semmelweis doctrine in Paris in 1851 had been unavailing. Of the Paris Maternité as late as 1864, Le Fort said:

The Maternité of Paris which I visited in the end of 1864 showed a condition of things which explained only too well its excessive mortality.

The principal ward contained a large number of beds placed in alcoves like English horse-stalls along each side. Ventilation was almost impossible. Floors and partitions were washed perhaps once a month . . . the ceilings showed that they had not been white-washed for many a long year. Lying-in women who became ill were transferred to an isolation room regardless of the nature of the illness—puerperal fever cases and patients affected with diarrheas, bronchitis, measles or any other eruptive fever. Midwife pupils attend normal lying-in patients and fever cases alike, and perform all the necessary manipulations for every class of case.

It is not astonishing that the Maternité of Paris has furnished a mortality without example in any European country. From 1860 to 1864 the patients numbered 9,886, of whom 1,226 died, equal to a mortality of 12.4 percent.

This hospital was administered by the Paris medical faculty, of which Karl Braun wrote in his refutation of Semmelweis' doctrine: "The Académie de Medicine of Paris under Orfila as president, in the year 1851, pronounced its decision against the theory of cadaveric infection. They also stated that the circumstances of midwifery practice at the *Maternité* and the *Clinique* were much the same as in the two divisions of the Lying-in Hospital of Vienna, and in both severe epidemics of puerperal fever occurred. They also expressed their opinion that chlorinated lime possessed no qualities to cause destruction of cadaveric molecules." (Sinclair's translation.)

In 1858 the same body of learned Frenchmen occupied themselves in a discussion of the nature and treatment of puerperal fever which lasted several months. Some of the opinions expressed are revealing. Depaul, admitting the contagiousness of puerperal fever, described it as analogous to septic infection but insisted that it was not a pyemia. The only preventive measure he could suggest was the building of smaller maternity hospitals. Beau argued against Depaul's description of the disease and suggested the use of large doses of quinine in treatment. Trousseau, in a lengthy address, arrived at the conclusion that puerperal fever was a specific malady, but that it did not attack lying-in women only. So it went. Cruveilhier and Velpeau made contributions of some value, but these were lost in the flood of words. Dubois, director of the Maternité and head of the obstetrical profession in France, mentioned the theory of Semmelweis twice and dismissed it both times as a doctrine now entirely discarded, even in the place where it had originated.

In England the Semmelweis doctrine continued to be widely approved and to exert considerable influence during these years, but little news of this favorable reception made its way to Budapest. It seems probable that Semmelweis never heard of an outstanding article by Dr. E. W. Murphy of the University College Hospital. Entitled "What is Puerperal Fever?" the paper appeared in the *Dublin Quarterly Journal of Medical Science* for August 1857. Under the heading *"Prophylaxis"* Murphy gave a thorough account of the Semmelweis method.

In Germany and Austria, where Semmelweis might naturally have expected the readiest acceptance, his doctrine was most generally attacked. The year 1857 was particularly fertile in these assaults. Veit of Rostock declared that puerperal fever was generally the result of epidemic influences, and that Semmelweis had found few followers. Anselm Martin of Munich described a puerperal epidemic which had broken out in the newly built lying-in hospital which he administered. Martin admitted the possibility of cadaveric infection, but seemed to think it was an inadequate explanation; like so many others he was ignorant of the full extent of the

Semmelweis doctrine. Joseph Spaeth of Vienna cannot, however, be excused on the ground of ignorance. On the very scene of the original discovery there were people and records readily at hand to give him whatever information he desired on Semmelweis. Yet in his *Kompendium der Geburtshilfe*, while admitting the possibility of infection by decomposed animal matter, he said not a word of the means devised by Semmelweis to prevent such infection.

With justice could Karl Braun write, in his *Lehrbuch der Geburtshilfe*, which also appeared in 1857, that the "hypothesis of cadaveric infection"—he did not name Semmelweis— had been almost entirely discarded in Germany and France. He included England, also, but in that, as we have seen, he was wrong.

The doctrine was spreading, in a way, for even opposition kept it alive, and often there appeared in medical journals here and there further proof of it. What was needed was another Paul preaching it from the housetops. And the one who could best accomplish the task at last decided to undertake it. Semmelweis resolved, in the fall of 1857, to prepare his own belated account of the discovery he had made. He had multitudinous notes and records, and he began to give what time he could spare to the difficult business of putting these materials in order. He wrote numerous letters, also, in 1858, to prominent obstetricians, inquiring about the results they had observed from the use of his prophylaxis. The answers, as they came, contributed little to his peace. Worse than those which deliberately denied his doctrine were those polite letters which showed misunderstanding of his thesis or a slighting opinion of its value. He was driven to labor ever more steadily toward the full publication of his beliefs in answer to all doubters. On January 2 and 23 and May 16, 1858, he lectured in Hungarian before the Pest medical society on the etiology of childbed fever. The lectures were published in *Orvosi Hetilap*.

The first Semmelweis child was born on October 14, 1858. Realizing that the chances of infection if the delivery took place in his own home were far less than in the more uncertain atmosphere of a hospital, he kept his wife at home. Over to the Semmelweis house went the round little bowls, half filled with white sand, and the bottles of the pungent solution of chloride of lime. Ludwig von Markusovszky, who had undertaken the care of Frau Semmelweis, rolled up his sleeves and washed his hands in the little bowls, until there was no question of transmission of any infective material to the young mother.

The labor and the delivery were long and hard, but finally it was over. The baby was given his father's name, Ignaz, and the parents rejoiced in him. Thirty-six hours later they found him dead in his cradle. The autopsy established the cause: hydrocephalus. The sorrow was hard to bear.

Chapter 14

Die AEtiologie and the *Offene Briefe*

WHEN HE began to recover from the loss of the child, Semmelweis turned his energies to improving the buildings in which his clinic was housed. In the latter part of 1858 he addressed a *Gesuch* (request) to his professional colleagues and to the high Imperial Royal Statthaltereiabtheilung in Budapest, the department which controlled the hospitals. It was his desire to move his clinic from the extremely unsanitary and inadequate part of the hospital which was allotted to his use. This time he took no chance of having his request stagnate on the desk of von Tandler. He went directly over the director's head to the department of the government controlling such affairs. His petition read, in part:

The only alternatives left to the professor of midwifery are either hermetically to close the windows and so permit the patients to suffer from vitiated air rendered still worse by the great crowd of students, or by opening the windows to admit to the patients air loaded with decomposed organic animal matter. . . .

The fact that cases of puerperal fever occur more frequently in the lying-in hospitals than among the population outside is known not only to the medical profession but also to the laity, and in official documents the lying-in hospital has been called a "murder hole" even by the non-medical officers themselves. Considering the fact that puerperal fever rages in the lying-in hospital the question has repeatedly been raised whether it would not be more humane to close the hospital altogether [Semmelweis is here referring to lying-in hospitals in Europe as a class, since such a condition obviously did not exist in his own institution].

Only a dreadful dilemma has saved lying-in hospitals from destruction. It is certain that a large number of the patients in lying-in hospitals are carried off in the bloom of life by puerperal fever. Without lying-in hospitals a larger number of women would remain well, but then would begin the anxiety with regard to the maintenance of themselves and their infants, and as a consequence of their necessity, the result would be crime, abortion, child exposure and desertion, and child murder. (Sinclair's translation.)

He went on to detail how he had discovered the cause of the disease and the method by which it could be prevented. He explained the causes of the outbreaks of disease at Budapest and how, as a result of these, opposition had been strengthened, closing with the sentence: "Hence it arises that the spread of the *Lehre* is hindered and the human race must suffer from the pestilence for a longer time than would have been the case if the success at the Obstetric Clinic at Budapest could have borne stronger witness to the truth of the Doctrine."

And then early in 1859 Marie Semmelweis again became pregnant and on November 20 the child was born. It was a little girl this time, a tiny fragile blond creature. Mariska brought happiness once more to her harrased father, but not for long. When she was four months old, illness came. Semmelweis dismissed his classes and took up a vigil at the bedside. Medicine had no help to offer, and the child grew steadily worse. It was soon evident that she had peritonitis and on the third day, March 15, 1860, she died. The parents, once more alone, consoled each other as best they could.

Being an extraordinarily capable physician, Semmelweis must naturally have wondered if some deficiency in his own body might not be carried over to his children, an hereditary taint which doomed them before they were born. But there was no immediate evidence of such a stigma. And, indeed, death rates in young children were distressingly high all over the world in that day.

Although tragedy and despair seemed constant companions, had Semmelweis stopped to evaluate his life he must have felt a certain sense of pride and satisfaction. In spite of his defeats he had accomplished much. He had saved many lives in Vienna and now he was saving many more in Budapest. Looking back over the past years he could have seen that he had done much to foster the spread of his beloved *Lehre*. More than a thousand midwives and Hungarian doctors had been instructed in his clinic and had gone out to practice his methods of antisepsis. They were a small but well trained army, bringing enlightenment where was darkness, bearing witness that the life of Dr. Ignaz Philipp Semmelweis had not been lived in vain.

Yet his pride cannot have been of long duration. He had placed his doctrine in the hands of the future, but all the authorities of the present seemed determined to stifle it. Still another opponent had entered the arena in 1858, Virchow of Berlin, a man like Semmelweis in that he was consumed by the fire of an uncompromising desire to know the truth. A revolutionary at the same time when Semmelweis was wearing the uniform of the Academic Legion, Virchow had been forced to flee for his life. Virchow was a great scientist and is known as the father of cellular pathology. Yet he presumed to step out of his field and to speak on the nature and etiology of puerperal fever before a group of Berlin obstetricians. His belief, which carried all the weight of his great fame and no truth at all, was that puerperal-fever epidemics resulted from the coincidence of certain weather conditions with the presence of a group of related diseases.

Virchow was to admit the infectious nature of puerperal fever and to make partial amends by a mention of Semmelweis at a later date, but meanwhile his enormous influence in medical circles on the continent had placed a new barrier in the way of obstetric progress. To Virchow, in *Die Ætiologie,* Semmelweis made probably the most scathing reply outside of his famous *Open Letters:*

To say nothing of my students, of medical practitioners and surgeons, there are at present 823 of my pupil midwives carrying on midwifery practice in Hungary, who know better than Virchow why the majority of epidemics of puerperal fever occur in winter, who know better than Virchow what to do in order to prevent puerperal fever when patients suffering from erysipelatous, croupous, putrid and purulent inflammation are committed to their care; who, more enlightened than the members of the Berlin Obstetrical Society, would laugh in derision at Virchow if he gave them a lecture on epidemic puerperal fever.

Largely as a result of his *Gesuch* describing the terrible conditions in the clinic at Pest, the Lying-in Hospital was removed early in 1860 to more suitable surroundings outside the city. The new quarters were not much better than the old: they were located on the second floor over the Surgery Clinic, and despite the increase of space there was no separate room available for the isolation of infectious cases. The worn and ragged fittings of the old hospital were removed to the new, and Semmelweis found it necessary to accommodate many of his patients on wooden benches or on straw spread on the floor. Yet he and his loyal staff succeeded in conquering these difficulties; during the school year 1859-60 there were only five fatal cases of puerperal fever out of 520 patients, a rate of 0.9%. In the same period 58 students and 199 midwives were instructed in clinical midwifery.

Such cares as these would have been more than enough for most men, yet Semmelweis continued to find time for work on his book. He read eagerly the letters which came in from the obstetricians and other scientists to whom he had written, as well as all new articles bearing in any way upon his discovery. Each was incorporated in the growing pile of manuscript, accompanied by his comments. His habitual patient logic more and more frequently gave way to the vehemence of exasperation. Thus he wrote of an *Historical-Critical Exposition of the Pathology of Puerperal Fever,* published in 1859 by Silberschmidt, a mere disciple of Scanzoni: "Du lieber Gott, when will puerperal fever cease to spread over whole provinces when by means of such unconscientious disingenuous opposition the medical practitioners scattered over whole provinces are befooled!"

One day early in 1860, as Dr. Hirschler, who was a close friend of Semmelweis and Markusovszky, was strolling through the streets of Pest, an excited and disheveled man rushed up and seized him by the arm. It was Semmelweis. Hirschler was too accustomed to the eccentricities of his friend to protest as he was taken to the latter's house and dumped into a chair in the study. Semmelweis jerked open a drawer and took from it a pile of manuscript, from which he began to read:

The object of this Treatise is to set forth historically the observations made in the Clinic, and to explain how I began to doubt the truth of the prevalent teaching with regard to Puerperal Fever. . . . It may be considered a proof of my aversion to polemics that I have left unanswered so many attacks, but I believed that I could leave the truth to open the way for itself. After waiting for thirteen years I find that the amount of progress has not been made which is necessary for the welfare of mankind.

He was reading from the newly written preface to his

book. The following months were spent in busy writing, and it was August before he gave up adding new chapters and sent the manuscript off to the printer. In October 1860, the work was published, with the date 1861.

He who had abhorred writing proved to be a prodigious writer. *Die Ætiologie, der Begriff und die Prophylaxis des Kindbettfiebers* (The Etiology, Concept, and Prophylaxis of Puerperal Fever) is one of the most exhaustive medical documents ever written. About half of its 543 pages consist of a thorough but by no means systematic discussion of the subject as indicated by the title. Here Semmelweis drew together in a mass that seldom achieves the appearance of order all the facts and statistics he had compiled in fifteen years of labor and study. Extensive tables on the mortality in the Vienna Lying-in Hospital, accounts of epidemics in other institutions, observations drawn from obstetrical literature, all are drawn upon to support the reasoning, almost pathetic in its painstaking thoroughness. There is nothing dogmatic, nothing authoritarian, in the simple and straightforward style in which Semmelweis tells how he weighed observations and statistics in arriving at his theory and how further circumstances caused him to develop that theory. With a humility which his opponents might profitably have imitated, he made no assertion without drawing up a battalion of proofs to sustain it.

The second half of the book consisted of a review of his correspondence with various physicians and of opinions expressed in obstetrical literature for and against his doctrine. In introduction to this polemical section he admitted that the first half of the book was an adequate presentation of the facts he wished to convey, but added:

My Doctrine is not established in order that the book expounding it may moulder in the dust of a library: my Doctrine has a mission, and that is to bring blessings into practical social life. My Doctrine is produced in order that it may be disseminated by teachers of midwifery until all who practice medicine, down to the last village doctor and the last village midwife may act according to its principals; my doctrine is produced in order to banish terror from the lying-in hospitals, to preserve the wife to the husband, the mother to the child.

With this aim he found it necessary to enter directly into controversy despite his distaste for it. His doctine had been public property for many years, yet it had been misunderstood, misrepresented, rejected. If he was to secure its survival he must answer all attacks, and he proceeded to do so at great length and too often with violence.

The addition of this controversial matter was perhaps the worst of Semmelweis' errors in the preparation of *Die Ætiologie*. Few readers had the courage to plow through the pages of rambling discussion of theories and statistics in the first half of the book, but all turned avidly to the polemic section, scenting argument and scandal there. His loyal friends deplored his vehemence and frenzy, while opponents and enemies were enraged by it and did their utmost to stifle the book.

After publication Semmelweis sent copies to many medical societies and to the major obstetricians of Germany, France, and England, including all who might aid in the spread of his teaching. Then he waited for some sign that his book was fulfilling the function for which he had written it, and that obstetricians were coming to see the truth of his theory as he knew they inevitably would. Little such evidence was forthcoming at first. Only a few short notices appeared in the medical press, some of them uncomplimentary. *Froriep's Notizen* was an exception in describing the book as one of the most important medical documents of the period. Markusovszky and Fleischer published highly favorable reviews, but since they wrote in Hungarian they exerted little influence beyond the boundaries of their country.

Finally, his sensibilities wounded to the quick by the almost universal ignoring of his book, Semmelweis again took up his pen and wrote the first two of his *Offene Briefe* (Open Letters). He addressed the first to Spaeth of the Joseph's Academy in Vienna, who in reviewing the obstetrical literature of the preceding year for a medical yearbook (published March 20, 1861), had described as fundamental a contribution which stated the cause of puerperal fever to be inflammation of the Fallopian tube.

To Spaeth, Semmelweis wrote:

From these expressions of opinion the Herr Professor has given me the impression that his spirit has not been lighted up by the puerperal sun which arose in Vienna in the year 1847, although it shone so near to him.

This stubborn ignoring of my doctrine, this stubborn ruminating over errors, causes me to bestow upon you the following explanation:

I carry with me the consciousness that since the year 1847 thousands and thousands of lying-in women and sucklings have died who would not have died if I had not remained silent, but to every error concerning puerperal fever which has been spread the necessary corrections have been partly made. About that, Herr Professor, you can persuade yourself that I do not exaggerate when I say that thousands upon thousands of lying-in women and new-born infants have lost their lives, who might have been saved, if I simply recall to your memory what occurred even in the First and Second Divisions of the Lying-in Hospital of Vienna from the 1st of January, 1849, to the last day of Demember, 1858. . . .

Semmelweis then analysed the statistics of the Vienna hospital for the ten-year period following his own departure and arrived at the damning conclusion that no less than 1,924 patients had died from infection which could have been avoided if his own principles had been followed.

In this massacre you, Herr Professor, have participated. The homicide must cease, and with the object of bringing this homicide to an end, I shall keep watch, and every man who dares to spread dangerous errors regarding puerperal fever will find in me an active opponent. For me there is no other means of checking the murder than unsparingly to unmask my opponents; and no one whose heart is in the right place will blame me for making use of this means. (Sinclair's translation.)

The second open letter, published in a pamphlet with that to Spaeth (Pest, 1861), was addressed to Semmelweis' bitterest critic, except perhaps Braun, Scanzoni of Würzburg. Scanzoni had been silent for some years, but Semmelweis, no doubt rightly, considered him responsible for an article by his assistant Dr. Otto von Franqué which had appeared early in 1860. Describing the many puerperal fever cases at Würzburg during three months of 1859, von Franqué had declared the causes of the "epidemic" to be certain atmospheric influences.

To Scanzoni, Semmelweis wrote:

Herr Hofrath will have learned from my letter to Professor Späth that I have formed a determined resolution to put an end to the murderous practices, and to effect that object I have resolved to attack unsparingly all who dare to spread error regarding puerperal fever. . . .

The greatest service rendered by my Doctrine is that it teaches how the unhappiness wrought by the malady can be with certainty prevented; that it prescribes to the practitioner a recognized active method of prophylaxis. Your teaching, on the other hand, puts upon the practitioner the stamp of the Turk who, in fatalistic passive resignation, permits the disaster to overwhelm his lying-in patients.

And to Scanzoni's contention, in refutation of Semmelweis' doctrine, that the practitioners and midwives of his own Würzburg did not carry infection, he answered with biting scorn:

It is said that special attention must be drawn to the fact that the puerperal fever cases in Würzburg did not all occur in the practice of one doctor: naturally, for it is not one practitioner in Würzburg, but all who practise there, who are ignoramuses on the subject of puerperal fever prevention, and for the ignorance the professors of midwifery are to blame. . . . and in this matter, Herr Hofrath, you have sent all over Germany a considerable contingent of practitioners who will, in their ignorance, engage in homicidal practices.

He concludes with one of the most scathing denunciations ever made in writing:

Your teaching, Herr Hofrath, is based upon the dead bodies of lying-in women slaughtered through ignorance; and . . . I have formed the unshakeable resolution to put an end to this murderous work as far as lies in my power to do so. . . . If, however, Herr Hofrath, without having discussed my Doctrine as an opponent, you go on to write . . . in support of the doctrine of epidemic puerperal fever, to teach your students the doctrine of epidemic puerperal fever, I denounce you before God and the world as a murderer, and the History of Puerperal Fever will not do you an injustice when, for the service of having been the first to oppose my life-saving *Lehre* it perpetuates your name as a medical Nero. (Sinclair's translation.)

Semmelweis sent a copy of his first two open letters to Eduard von Siebold, Professor of Obstetrics at Göttingen. They had become acquainted during Semmelweis' assistantship in Vienna, and von Siebold had since been a welcome guest at his Pest home. But in 1861, von Siebold published an article in which he took a stand against Semmelweis. Though he had probably heard Semmelweis' personal exposition of his theory and certainly possessed a copy of *Die Ætiologie*, von Siebold persisted in the old error that Semmelweis thought cadaveric infection to be the principal, "indeed the sole source of puerperal epidemics." In his article he criticized the doctrine as too limited and censured the immoderate manner in which Semmelweis attacked all those who held opinions opposed to his own.

The third open letter was addressed to this one-time friend, and the mild phrases Semmelweis used made it clear that he was rather hurt than angered by von Siebold's defalcation:

> Herr Hofrath, I know you as a man of extremely kind disposition; I am convinced that it is not possible for you to do intentionally a thing disagreeable to any man. . . . I entreat you, Herr Hofrath, to acquire an intimate knowledge of the truth as it is set forth in my book, so that according to your kindly disposition you may be able to find support for new opinions in the bright faces of your lying-in patients and—in an empty deadhouse. (Sinclair's translation.)

Semmelweis included in this letter a proposal that a meeting of German obstetricians be held in the fall of 1861 to debate the question of puerperal fever. He expressed the confident belief that he could convert all present to his theory of the disease. Von Siebold made no answer to this letter or to the proposal of a meeting. He was ill at the time and died in October 1861. Not unnaturally he was vexed by Semmelweis' open rebuke, and he commented that Semmelweis had been scorched by the rays of the "puerperal sun." It could not be expected that publication of these letters by Semmelweis would make anyone feel more kindly toward him, in fact it was inevitable that they would make enemies and actually hinder the spread of his beloved *Lehre*.

The letter to von Siebold was published with a second open letter to Scanzoni. In his zeal, Semmelweis even stooped to capitalize upon misfortune, although perhaps legitimately, considering his motives, when he wrote of an epidemic which about this time ravaged Scanzoni's clinic at Würzburg:

> Herr Hofrath has been in the right for thirteen years because I have been silent for thirteen years; now I have broken the silence and I am in the right, and I shall so remain as long as the human female continues to bear children. To you, Herr Hofrath, nothing remains, if you would save your reputation or at least as much of it as remains to save, but to accept my *Lehre*. If you adhere to the doctrine of epidemic puerperal fever, then, with the advancement of knowledge, both pseudo-epidemics of puerperal fever and your reputation will disappear from the world. . . .

Some benefit has accrued from these two pseudo-epidemics of puerperal fever in your new lying-in hospital, provided with the very best furnishings and appliances: they have completely disposed of the proposals of ignorant Frenchmen to erect new lying-in hospitals as the only was of preserving the lives of the patients. You have demonstrated, Herr Hofrath, that in spite of a new hospital provided with the most modern furnishings and appliances, a good deal of homicide can be perpetrated where the required talent in that way exists. (Sinclair's translation.)

Copies of the two brochures of open letters were sent by Semmelweis to Dr. L. Kugelmann of Hannover, among others. In reply Semmelweis received a most complimentary letter, one of the few spots of brightness in the dark story. Kugelmann wrote that his study of *Die Ætiologie* had brought him to think of Semmelweis as another Jenner. As a token of respect he sent Semmelweis a copy of Jenner's *Inquiry into the Causes and Effects of the Variolae Vaccinae*, inscribed by Jenner to Professor Blumenbach of Göttingen. This and such other small compliments as he received earned from Semmelweis almost pathetic gratitude. They were all too few.

The birth of his third child in August 1861 briefly took his mind off his fight for recognition. This child was a girl and healthy; the father's spirits soared again. A son was to follow in 1862, and another daughter in 1864.

Yet these family joys were not sufficient to balance the goadings of despair at the reluctance of others to accept his doctrine. Already in the initial stages of the mental deterioration which was to dim the last years of his life, Semmelweis became markedly erratic in his behavior. His friends found him increasingly irritable and impatient in manner, quickly resentful of criticism, suspicious of their words and deeds.

A picture taken of him at about this time—he was only forty-three—shows a man already old. The bald dome of his head is fringed with gray hair; eyebrows and mustache are touched with white. And the eyes and mouth are set, the brow wrinkled, in a fixed expression of truculence, almost of suspiciousness. The contrast between this expression and the open, friendly look of another picture taken only four years before, apparently at the time of his marriage, is truly amazing. In that time sorrow and disappointment and mental strain had aged the man beyond belief.

Late in 1861 Dr. Breisky of Prague published a brief criticism on *Die Ætiologie,* which was notable not in itself but in its results. After a rebuke to Semmelweis for publishing his doctrine as if he were a prophet delivering a new Koran, Breisky went on to give a sarcastic statement of the Semmelweis theory and its proofs. The review was written throughout in a tone of scornful disbelief and was full of clever gibes. In reply Markusovszky published in *Orvosi Hetilap* a defense of Semmelweis which exceeded Semmelweis' own publications not only in clarity but also in sagacity. For Markusovszky maintained that while Semmelweis had hit upon the proper prophylactic measures and was undoubtedly on the right track as regarded the etiology and nature of puerperal fever, something was yet unknown. It was still to be learned, he pointed out, just what the nature of the organic material which produced the infection was, how it reached the organism, what physiological changes it wrought there, why it acted differently in different cases.

Markusovszky was in a sense predicting the future researches of Pasteur and the great bacteriologists. But Semmelweis could not join him in the vision: he had his eyes fixed immovably on the present, on the here-and-now reception of his doctrine. Once a clear and direct thinker, he had now become as much a dogmatic as any. And Markusovszky's article only made him suspect that his friend was not wholly loyal and devoted. His suspicions found expression one evening when Markusovszky and several other friendly colleagues were guests at his home. As always when Semmelweis was among physicians the talk finally turned to the subject of childbed fever, already recognized as a touchy one. Markusovszky rushed into a vehement attack on the opponents of the Semmelweis doctrine. Scarcely had he finished when he regretted every word; Semmelweis fell into an indescribable rage and thundered countless accusations at his faithful adherent. The less loyal friends watched the show with sarcastic smiles while Markusovszky with admirable patience endured the attack in silence.

One of the principal sources of the mental strain which was gradually undermining the sanity of Semmelweis was the ever-recurring thought of the countless women and babies who were dying in hospitals all over the world because his doctrine was not accepted. In his own clinic all was well: there he could supervise and persuade or force all comers into careful prophylactic measures. There was no puerperal fever at all in his clinic during the school year 1860-61. But Vienna! In the Second Clinic of the Vienna Lying-in Hospital where

Dr. Zipfel was now provisional director 35 out of 101 patients had died in the autumn of 1860. Zipfel's official report on the deaths was published in 1861; he denied any possibility of infection from decomposed animal matter; he insisted that the disease resulted from miasmas in the institution and suggested that it be closed. And in Karl Braun's clinic, the First Clinic where Semmelweis had made his great discovery, 113 women sickened of puerperal fever and 48 died within 45 days in the early autumn of 1861. Braun later reported that preventive measures had been taken, measures very like those recommended by Semmelweis, but that these had had no effect in stopping the epidemic. During the first half of November 48 out of 253 patients had contracted the fever.

From Prague came even worse news. In 1860, 3¾ % of the mothers and 18¾ % of the babies died; in 1861, 4% of the mothers and 22½ % of the babies. In Stockholm in 1860 40% of the lying-in women took puerperal fever and 16% died.

Again Semmelweis took up his pen. Now he addressed himself in an open letter to all professor of obstetrics (Ofen, 1862). After recapitulating at length the statistics and arguments of *Die Ætiologie,* he opened a furious attack on his opponents, Braun and Scanzoni in particular. The tone was that of a fanatic and the bitter words flowed without stint:

If the Professors of Obstetrics do not soon comply by instructing their students in my doctrine . . . then will I myself say to the helpless public: "You, father of a family, do you know what it is to summon an obstetrician or a midwife to your wife? . . . It is as much as to expose your wife and your yet unborn child to the danger of death. And if you do not wish to become a widower and if you do not wish that your still unborn child be inoculated with the germ of death, and if your children are not to lose their mother, then buy a single kreutzer's worth of chloride of lime, infuse it in some water, and do not allow the obstetrician and the midwife to examine your wife until they have washed their hands in the chlorine solution in your presence, and also do not permit the obstetrician and the midwife to make an internal examination until you have convinced yourself by touching their hands that the obstetrician and the midwife have washed so long that their hands have become slippery.

Words like these and many more flowed from the pen of Semmelweis. Perhaps he realized instinctively that his mind was beginning to fail and wrote furiously in order to make his doctrine better known before he lost the ability to do so. He was criticized for resorting to open letters, but actually there was little else he could do. Most of the important medical publications of Europe were closed to his writings, because of the enmity of such powerfully entrenched obstetricians as Karl Braun and Scanzoni. In the *Open Letters,* he performed a double function, too, in making this controversy known to those most concerned, the public.

But his newly discovered facility with the pen came too late to be of much immediate satisfaction to him. Where earlier his writing ability might well have been put to better use to spread his doctrine through the conventional scientific channels of medical journals and societies, it now ran against the stone wall of professional indifference and actual hate.

It was natural that small minds should hate one who could castigate them in such burning words as these open letters contain, and refuse to believe anything written by so vitriolic a pen. The tragedy of Semmelweis' life was to a large degree of his own making. He delayed too long in publicizing his discovery, and found too late the method by which his theories could be spread. In 1848 Skoda, Rokitansky, and Hebra pleaded with him to write the volume which finally appeared as *Die Ætiologie.* Even when it did appear, while one of the most remarkable scientific documents of all time, it was so long and wordy, countlessly reiterating the truth he was seeking to establish, that many sincere men were unable to assimilate its truths because of its very deficiencies. In Vienna he would have had the benefit of active editorial assistance, assistance which he might have taken then, but which later, irascible and already emotionally unstable, he did not use.

His defense came too late to bring him anything except more unhappiness and heartbreak. Not in his own lifetime was he to have the satisfaction of knowing that no woman in Europe was dying in all the lying-in hospitals because an ignorant doctor or midwife brought infection to her on his unwashed hands.

Chapter 15

The Fourth Trial, Death

THROUGH THE YEARS of his tenure in Budapest, Semmelweis had revived the interest in gynecology, the study of diseases peculiar to the reproductive apparatus of women, which he had been forced to submerge in Vienna and again in Budapest except during his period at St. Rochus. This was a natural sphere for him, since he was thoroughly versed in the anatomy and pathology of this aspect of medicine. His friends encouraged him in this new field, hoping to draw his attention away from obstetrics and the bitter storm of controversy aroused by his publications, particularly the *Open Letters*.

There was a fertile field for progress in gynecologic surgery at this time. Although operations had been performed *per vaginam* for many centuries, Semmelweis had himself been impressed first with the problem of childbed fever when a woman from whom Chiari had removed a pedunculated tumor of the *cervix uteri* developed typical puerperal fever. Only a few daring individuals opened the abdominal cavity to attack the diseased pelvic structures in that region. Fully fifty years before, Ephraim MacDowell in the United States had performed his now famous ovariotomy, and even before him some English surgeons had dared to attack abdominal tumors directly. But the operation of *laparotomy*, opening the abdominal cavity, was still far from frequent and not by any means always successful.

One deterrent to successful abdominal surgery had always been the likelihood of severe infection following the operation, with peritonitis a not infrequent complication. But Semmelweis had conquered this particular problem himself with his antisepsis and it was natural that he should introduce his technique of antisepsis in gynecologic surgery, as he had in obstetrics. Haller had mentioned the importance of the Semmelweis method in surgery almost fifteen years before in his annual report of activities in the Allgemeine Krankenhaus. But like Semmelweis' prophylaxis in obstetrics, the revolutionary character of the discovery for surgical practice had not been realized by his hearers. Surgeons continued to operate and patients continued to fall victim to infections. Only in

141

England—and not generally there—did surgeons realize the importance of the simple principle of cleanliness. Thus some English surgeons had for a long time operated with considerably less mortality than was the rule in Europe, where in Vienna, it was sometimes as high as ninety per cent.

Semmelweis' own description of his technique of prophylaxis of the hands for example, at that time the most fertile source of infection in surgical operations, is so simple that its application to surgical work should have been obvious to anyone:

"The necessity for disinfecting the hand will . . . always be present, and in order to completely attain this object, it is necessary to oil the hand well before any contact with decomposed matter, so that the decomposed matter may not penetrate into the pores of the skin; after such occupation the hand must be washed with soap, and then exposed to the action of a chemical agent, capable of destroying the decomposed matter not yet removed; we use for this purpose chloride of lime and wash until the hands are slippery.

"A hand so treated is completely disinfected. Carriers of decomposed matter are not only the examining finger, but all objects, contaminated with decomposed matter, which come in contact with the genitalia of patients; these objects must be disinfected before their contact with the genitalia or must not be used; in this class belong instruments, bed-pans, bed-linen, sponges, etc. etc."

This is an almost exact description of surgical asepsis of today with the difference only that sterilization was achieved by chemicals, rather than by heat.

Since Semmelweis had already shown the exact method by which infection is transmitted, he undoubtedly recognized that the same method of transmission accounted for the high incidence of infection following surgery. He applied these principles to his own practice of gynecologic surgery and they were also applied by his Budapest colleague, von Balassa, for he and Semmelweis worked together actively in surgery and gynecology.

Actually Semmelweis' concept of antisepsis as applied to surgery had been clear since his discovery in 1847 and the subsequent application of it during his period as Assistant in the First Division. In *Die Ætiologie*, he says:

And how deplorable also is the condition of the patients cared for in the gynecological department, as proved by the reports on the results of the department, and taking the case of the uterine polyps only . . . how often such patients die of pyemia after the excision. I have directed a gynecological department for six years, I take all cases reporting with uterine polyps during the five years since I have been professor, I have frequently had the opportunity to operate on uterine polyps in private practice, I have removed this specified number of polyps by excision. Not only have I not a single case of death to deplore, I have not even seen a single significant case of illness after excision, although there were polyps with pedicles a hand's breadth in length. These favorable results I ascribe only to the fact that I operate with clean hands.

Sir William J. Sinclair gives a graphic picture of gynecologic practice in Hungary at the time when Semmelweis introduced antiseptic practices into surgery at the University of Budapest:

Singular light is thrown on the state of gynecology in Hungary by the fact that Semmelweis was the first to perform ovariotomy in that country: this was in June, 1863.

There can be little doubt that it was Markusovszky who inspired the enterprising incident. At that time the operations of Charles Clay, of Manchester, Baker Brown and Spencer Wells, of London, and Thomas Keith, of Edinburgh, had attracted the attention of all the cultural lands of Europe and America [he fails to mention the far earlier operation of Ephraim MacDowell in the United States in December, 1809], and drew streams of medical visitors to witness them. Among these visitors was Markusovszky of Buda-Pesth, who came back with glowing accounts of what he had seen and heard. Semmelweis appears to have performed this first ovariotomy according to the method described to him by his friend, finishing a very unfavorable case with the external clamp on the pedicle (the stalk upon which the tumor grew), the method employed in those days even by some of the best operators. V. Balassa, the professor of surgery, acted as assistant, in the presence of most of the faculty of medicine of the University, and a large company of medical practitioners (*einer zahlreichen Hörerschaft*). The patient died fifty-two hours after the operation and the autopsy showed the condition of parts that was to be expected—under the circumstances.

In spite of this failure, the operation was taken up in Buda-Pesth and in Hungary generally, and the results in the hands of V. Balassa, and later of Tauffer and Kezmarszky and others, soon became as favorable as any in Europe. They had only had a bad start.

Through his new interest in gynecological surgery, Semmelweis attained comparative peace for a time. It must have been a relief not to spend his every waking hour cursing those who fought against him, trying to find a new way of spreading his beloved *Lehre*. For a time he became almost apathetic, his controversies forgotten, his time taken completely by his children, his charming wife, and his new work. Protected by antisepsis he could now undertake operations which would have been murder in the contaminated hands of ordinary surgeons on the continent. Had he lived, he might well have achieved a new fame eclipsing that which he had earned as an obstetrician.

But the long years of controversy, the bitter disappointments he had suffered, the memory of the women he had seen die, first because he could not discover the cause of their dying, and later because others could not understand the simple principles he evolved to prevent their dying,—all these things were burdens which would have broken down the barriers of a sanity greater than his. His ordinary tendency to moodiness became accentuated. There were days when he hardly spoke to his colleagues, lecturing in an almost unintelligible monotone to the students, and breaking out every now and then into a passionate harangue for no apparent reason.

His wife and his friends worried for his sanity and began to watch him closely, fearful that in a moment of passion he might do himself harm. His behavior steadily grew more strange, his preoccupation more intense. At a dinner at the home of a friend, he rose suddenly from his place at the table and began to harangue the group in an unintelligible torrent of impassioned words. With help his wife managed to get him home where he quieted down.

Hoping to prevent further occurrence of these distressing outbreaks by removing him to a quiet place, the Semmelweis family went out to the country for a short while. There he was quiet, almost apathetic, as his wife expressed it: "like a good sick child." And when they returned to the city he seemed more like his normal self and even resumed classes once more.

One afternoon, at a meeting of the faculty, he seemed quite normal. The business of the afternoon was the selection of an assistant in Semmelweis' own department. But when it came his turn to speak, he suddenly turned pale and leaped to his feet. Taking a piece of paper from his pocket, he read from the beginning of the oath which the midwives recited on the day that they took up their functions. In the face of this and many other like occurrences, it could no longer be denied that the brilliant obstetrician was mentally ill.

In July, at a conference of members of the family, Markusovszky, and Hirschler, it was decided that Semmelweis should be taken to Vienna at once, to be placed under the care of Dr. Riedel, an alienist there whose sanatorium for mental cases was famous throughout Austria.

On July 31, 1865, the sad journey began. Semmelweis, his wife, and their baby daughter, Antonie, accompanied by an uncle and Semmelweis' Assistant, Dr. Bathory, took the train to Vienna. The trip was uneventful and Hebra, warned by telegraph, met them at the Vienna station. He had engaged two carriages; in the second rode Semmelweis, between Bathory and Hebra. They drove first to Hebra's home, and during the drive Hebra invited his friend to visit the new sanatorium. Semmelweis consented and after a brief pause to speak to Frau Hebra, the men drove on. In the sanatorium Semmelweis displayed great interest in the arrangements, asking several questions. A physician held Semmelweis in talk so that Hebra and the others could depart unnoticed. When Semmelweis tried to leave, saying that he must hurry back to his practice, he was forcibly restrained. He fell into a fit of delirium and six attendants could scarcely hold him. He was confined to a strait-jacket and put in a dark room.

The next day Dr. Riedel refused to allow Frau Semmelweis to see her husband and she returned heartbroken to Vienna where she suffered an illness of six weeks. This period saw the death of Semmelweis. The sanatorium physician discovered an infected wound on the middle finger of his right hand, apparently the result of a gynecological operation. The wound became gangrenous, abscesses appeared in the armpit, a metastasis formed between the muscles of the left breast and invaded the pleura. Death resulted on the 13th of August, 1865.

As if Fate had decided to write with a pen dipped in irony this last chapter in a life which it had dealt some of its bitterest blows, Semmelweis himself died from the same infection as had Kolletschka, in whose death he had seen the sudden glare of the "puerperal sun."

Along the same sad path which he had watched many a mother travel, as well as many a promising doctor, the body of Semmelweis was carried to the post-mortem table of the

Allgemeine Krankenhaus, where two of Rokitansky's assistants performed the autopsy, revealing the unmistakable progress of pyemia.

Semmelweis developed a life-saving principle and gave his own life in final proof of it.

Chapter 16

The Fate of the Doctrine

PROBABLY THE LAST ENCOURAGEMENT Semmelweis had in his unhappy fight for the lives of mothers was the report of a discussion held in St. Petersburg on July 4, 1863. Arneth, long one of Semmelweis' most ardent supporters, had been in an important position in St. Petersburg for some time and took part in the proceedings. Hugenberger, who directed the discussion, reported the experience of the Midwives' Clinic of the Lying-in Hospital in which the mortality from puerperal fever was 3.8% while that within the entire city was 0.7%. He concluded that, "regarding the most important causes of puerperal fever in the *Hebammeninstitute,* we see that the three sources of infection according to Semmelweis, are the principal; the rest of the cases are mere exceptions."

It must have been a source of considerable satisfaction to Semmelweis to learn that, as a result of this meeting, every Russian midwife was ordered to apply the Semmelweis prophylaxis in the care of her maternity cases. As Semmelweis said of the midwives of Hungary, they knew more about preventing puerperal fever than the professors of some of the greatest clinics of Europe. Hugenberger outlined the method by which the *Lehre* was to be propagated when he wrote to Semmelweis: "You will see from this how many followers you have in the Far North, and how strongly the younger men support you. By that alone much is gained, for it is in their hands that the future lies." The last writings of Semmelweis consisted of articles on the St. Petersburg episode which he contributed to *Orvosi Hetilap.*

After the death of Semmelweis, his doctrine made little progress of itself. In America the controversy centering around the two articles of Oliver Wendell Holmes died away. In Britain where cleanliness had so long been general among obstetricians, the Semmelweis doctrine, though sponsored by Simpson and other prominent physicians, was gradually forgotten. As late as 1870 many of the speakers at a debate before the Obstetrical Society of London held puerperal fever to be not a simple pyemia, but a disease arising from a special condition in parturient women. In France, despite the labors of Arneth in 1851, the theory of cadaveric infection was rejected or ignored and conditions at the Paris Maternité remained in a shocking state in the mid-sixties and later.

Even in Budapest, where for almost fifteen years Semmelweis had trained young doctors and midwives in his prophylaxis, his immediate successors let his cause suffer. Dr. Johann Diescher, appointed to Semmelweis' chair at the University, was not even a specialist in gynecology and obstetrics. Dr. Walla, the incumbent at St. Rochus, was at best a lukewarm supporter of the Semmelweis doctrine. Puerperal fever returned to Budapest, not to be banished until Dr. Fleischer, once Semmelweis' assistant, succeeded Walla, and von Kezmarszky, another adherent, replaced Diescher. And though there were many faithful in Hungary, the spread of knowledge from this country was hampered by the intense nationalism which led to publication of scientific information in the Hungarian language. Hence the fervent defense of Semmelweis by Markusovszky, published in *Orvosi Hetilap*, probably had little effect beyond Hungary's borders.

In the latter half of the nineteenth century, Vienna was the medical center of the universe. And so when the Austrian government planned to erect a new lying-in hospital in Prague, it was natural that Vienna was well represented upon the commission of medical experts called upon in 1863 to give advice. Skoda, Rokitansky, and Oppolzer represented Vienna; Virchow, Berlin; and Lange, Heidelberg. The authorities demanded a direct answer to the question of whether or not the contagious theory of origin and extension of puerperal fever was firmly established.

The replies showed a rather surprising lack of agreement, in the face of Semmelweis' clear-cut demonstration fifteen years before. Skoda, Rokitansky, and Oppolzer upheld contagion. Virchow, whose influence was considerable, held to a theory of predisposition of the lying-in woman to inflammations. Lange denied the contagiousness from a specific product. Others had equally indefinite theories. Only a year later, however, Virchow espoused the Semmelweis doctrine, a considerable step forward in its spread. As one of the leading pathologists and medical editors of the Continent, Virchow's opinions carried a great deal of weight, whether or not he knew what he was talking about as he probably did not in the puerperal fever question, since he was in no sense a clinician.

Professor Bartsch had been director of the Midwives' Clinic in the Allgemeine Krankenhaus at Vienna during the tenure of Semmelweis as Assistant. He was succeeded in 1861 by Professor Spaeth, who had opposed the *Lehre* in the beginning. Like Karl Braun, Semmelweis' successor in the First Division, Spaeth professed not to believe in prophylaxis but actually practiced it to a considerable degree. Spaeth seems to have been more diligent in prophylaxis, however, for from a pre-prophylaxis mortality of 16% he achieved a record of 0.5%, a clear-cut demonstration of its value. In February 1864, he read a paper before the Vienna Society of Physicians in which he enumerated the accomplishments of Semmelweis, finishing with the following very significant statement considering that it came from the Professor of Midwifery in the foremost medical school in the world:

> . . . . I venture also to express quite distinctly the opinion that there is no longer remaining a teacher of midwifery who is not in his own heart convinced of the truth of the doctrine of Semmelweis, even when he still expresses himself as decidedly opposed to it. . . . and I ask, who treats his cases in a manner not in accordance with the principles of Semmelweis? Why does everyone preach that the utmost cleanliness is necessary? Why does everybody wish the hands with which the examinations are made to be thoroughly disinfected by a solution of chloride of lime or permanganate of potash? . . . Why do we attend to ventilation? Why do we see to it that bed-linen and utensils are perfectly clean? Why do we isolate infected cases? (Sinclair's translation.)

In science, claiming another's discovery as one's own is perhaps as sincere a form of flattery as imitation. If so, the memory of Semmelweis was certainly flattered by many who wrote about obstetrics and puerperal fever in the decades following his discovery. A long list of obstetricians, like Karl Braun, claimed to oppose him, but brought forward as their own, concepts first enunciated by Semmelweis. For example, Hirsch, Professor of Medicine in the University of Berlin, wrote in 1864 supporting Semmelweis, but claimed the following concept as his own:

Moreover the infecting substance may come from the pus and ichor generated in various forms of disease. Again experience teaches us that infection may take place by means of the patient's clothes, or through instruments, sponges, bed-linen, bedding and the like; and, to make the pile complete, by the air entering with the finger or instrument introduced into the vagina or uterus, perhaps even by means of air entering by aspiration. (Sinclair's translation.)

Actually Semmelweis had clearly stated just this principle several years before in *Die Ætiologie*.

One of the firmest opponents of Semmelweis in the early history of the doctrine of prophylaxis was Professor G. Veit. But in 1867 we find him writing in Virchow's *Handbuch:* "The explanation of puerperal fever as a resorption fever produced by infection by means of decomposed animal material, has in recent years been accepted by an ever widening circle, and erelong it will meet with no opponents."

A bitter opponent of Semmelweis, and the target of perhaps the most vitriolic of the *Open Letters,* was Professor Scanzoni. Because of Scanzoni's high academic position and his accomplishments in the field of obstetrics, notably in the technique of forceps delivery, his opinions carried considerable weight. In the beginning he had opposed Semmelweis at every point, but in the new edition of his *Lehrbuch* in 1867, he stated:

We are still of the opinion that it is chiefly miasmatic influences in lying-in hospitals whch lie at the root of the diseases most frequently affecting lying-in women. . . . It affords real satisfaction to observe that Semmelweis, who at first attributed puerperal infection in lying-in hospitals almost exclusively to cadaveric poison, felt compelled later to assign a suitable recognition to other ways of infection. . . . Further we cannot and will not leave unmentioned that Semmelweis, by his restless and self-sacrificing efforts in this field, has achieved a great service to lying-in women in our hospitals. . . . (Sinclair's translation.)

In this decidedly left-handed way, Scanzoni acknowledged the truth of Semmelweis' contentions in regard to puerperal fever.

Boehr, writing in May 1868, and von Winckel in 1869 repeated the common error in stating that Semmelweis attributed puerperal fever entirely to cadaveric infection. It is strange how this concept keeps cropping up, in spite of Semmelweis' repeated statements describing a number of other sources of infection and his experiences with the contaminated linen, the carious bone, and many other means of contamination. It is almost as if the obstetricians in question had deliberately ignored the truth, in their attempt to discredit its source. Some of this deliberate ignorance may stem, it must be admitted, from the decidedly intemperate language which Semmelweis himself had used to lash out at those who did not immediately accept his beloved *Lehre*.

By 1881, even the most bitter opponent of Semmelweis, Karl Braun, could no longer ignore the truth, but in his *Lehrbuch* of 1882, he still managed to sidestep any open avowal of the Semmelweis theory, although it is a known fact that he had been using the Semmelweis principles of antisepsis—albeit somewhat lackadaisically—in the Lying-in Hospital of Vienna. He says:

According to Semmelweis (1847) and Lange (1862), puerperal fever arises from a blood disease produced by infection from decomposed animal matter. . . .

Most gynecologists of recent times have expressed the opinion that puerperal fever may arise spontaneously, and that it then becomes infectious to healthy women during labor or in childbed, and that the infection may then be spread by foul air penetrating inside the genitals or *by the introduction of unclean hands or instruments.* (Italics author's. Sinclair's translation.)

Professor W. A. Freund, in 1885, paid tribute to Semmelweis and his greatness, and finished with this pungent observation: "When Fate calls upon such natures to play the part of prophets, the performance is always a tragedy. Fortunate for mankind if the prophecy is not overwhelmed with the prophet."

Chapter 17

Triumph

THE JUSTIFICATION of the work of Semmelweis came with the discovery by Louis Pasteur of the identity of bacteria as the real culprit in the causation of puerperal fever.

Dr. Emile Roux described the occasion on March 11, 1879, when Pasteur proclaimed his discovery of the real cause of puerperal fever:

One day, in a discussion on puerperal fever at the Academy, one of his (Pasteur's) most weighty opponents was eloquently enlarging upon the causes of epidemics in lying-in hospitals: Pasteur interrupted him: "None of those things cause the epidemic; it is the nursing and medical staff who carry the microbe from an infected woman to a healthy one." And as the orator replied that he feared that microbe would never be found, Pasteur went to the blackboard and drew a diagram of the chain-like organism, saying, "There, that is what it is like."

Pasteur had found the streptococcus in the lochia of dying patients and also in the bloodstream, bringing forth the final evidence in support of the Semmelweis theory of a concrete infecting agent. Had Semmelweis been alive then, he might well have said, as did Oliver Wendell Holmes to Dr. Chadwick in 1883: ". . . I shrieked my warning louder and longer than any of them and I am pleased to remember that I took my ground on the existing evidence, before the little army of microbes was marched up to support my position."

Even before Pasteur hit upon the precise agent of puerperal fever, however, Semmelweis' work had been carried to its fulfillment by yet another worker. On August 12, 1865, the day before the death of Semmelweis, Joseph Lister of Glasgow, acting on conclusions he had reached on reading certain memoirs by Louis Pasteur, used carbolic acid as an antiseptic in treating a case of compound fracture. The wound healed rapidly, without suppuration. Lister continued his experiments with complete success and published in 1867 his report, "A New Method of Treating Compound Fractures, Abscesses, Etc." Shortly thereafter he addressed the British Medical Association "On the Antiseptic Principle in the Practice of Surgery," giving a full account of his development of the first rational treatment of wounds in the history of surgery, a treatment based on a sound knowledge of the etiology and pathogenesis of suppuration.

No biography of Semmelweis would be complete without an evaluation of his contribution to antiseptic practice in surgery as well as obstetrics, and a considerable controversy raged on just this point during the years following Lister's announcement of his success with antisepsis. Actually neither can claim priority, for both but aided in the inevitable progress toward modern aseptic technique.

There is no question that Semmelweis practiced antiseptic surgery fully fifteen years before Lister, and he therefore deserves a certain amount of priority. And to the student of medical history, the truth seems to be that for his age and his place, Semmelweis' discovery was more of an accomplishment than that of Lister, who had the stout foundation of Pasteur's discoveries on which to proceed.

From Lister on, antiseptic science advanced steadily. There were opponents, but Lister succeeded, through writing and teaching, in pressing home the truth. The result is to be seen in the complicated aseptic ritual of today, in which the surgeon is accoutred in gown, mask, and gloves, his instruments sterilized, the very air of the operating room purified by ultraviolet irradiation. And not the surgeon alone, but the obstetrician as well. What joy it would have brought to the heart of Semmelweis if he could have seen his simple prophylaxis thus developed. Yet he prophesied the triumph, though he did not live to see it. In a brief "Nachwort" to *Die Ætiologie* he wrote:

When I with my present convictions look back upon the Past, I can only dispel the sadness which falls upon me by gazing into that happy Future when within the lying-in hospitals, and also outside of them, only cases of self-infection will occur. . . .
But should it not be given to me, which God forbid, to behold this happy time with my own eyes, the conviction that this time will come without fail sooner or later after me, will still soothe my hour of death.

Ludwig von Markusovszky, in the obituary of Semmelweis which he wrote for *Orvosi Hetilap,* made a just analysis of his friend's accomplishment:

He was one of those mortals not always happy, but he was favored by fate, inasmuch as it was given to him to enrich science with a new idea, and thereby to confer upon humanity an immeasurably important service. And what still further enhances the service in this respect is the circumstance that his discovery was no mere stroke of chance, but the result of a living conclusion and conviction, evolved out of scientific observation and knowledge. (Sinclair's translation.)

As Fritsch of Breslau wrote of *Die Ætiologie* in 1884:

In the history of Midwifery there is a dark page, and it is headed "Semmelweis"! What man could close his eyes to the powerful impression of his book? Even now at the present time there are whole pages of his deductions which might stand in the most modern work. And the annihilating logic of his statistics!

We younger men for whom antipathies are unthinkable, to whom the reading of coarse tirades about "genius misunderstood," was only tedious we often find it incomprehensible that the logical conclusions of the doctrine of infection were nowhere drawn: I mean the local treatment; it was the keystone of the arch, the crown of the whole structure . . . The efficient application of disinfection midwifery owes without doubt to surgery; most certainly it ought to have been the reverse. If the conclusions and counsels of Semmelweis had been followed, then the truth of his doctrine would have been demonstrated in the compelling language of statistics, and so perhaps Obstetrics would have stood in the forefront of the greatest advance in Medicine which has been made since physicians and physic came into existence. (Sinclair's translation.)

The whole story of Semmelweis is a valuable lesson for the worker in science. For he patiently made his way from known to unknown, along the path of careful investigation and elimination, a method not original with him, of course, but beautifully illustrated in his procedure. And his very mistakes—mistakes in method, in interpretation, and worst of all in the belief that his doctrine would make its own way in the world—these stand as warnings to every serious scientist.

For a scientist must learn that it is not enough to make a great discovery. He must teach mankind to apply it to their own betterment. And that task is often far more difficult than the actual search for truth.

As a martyr to the world's stupidity, Semmelweis is one of the great tragic figures of all history. As a man and a scientist, his memory is glorious. In his own time innumerable lives were saved because of his discovery, both through his own efforts and those of his students. Had he lived but two decades longer he would have seen his theory fully explained and accepted, his prophylaxis used throughout the world. He might well have fathered antiseptic surgery himself. As it was, he died in the very dawn of a new age of surgery and midwifery, and other men carried to victory the fight which he began.

Index

155

only mean one thing; the infecting agent was reaching the mothers after the child was born, not during labor and delivery. The logical place to look for the cause, then, was in the wards where the mothers lay during the nine-day period before they were hustled out so that others might take their place.

And here he found the damning evidence at once in the sheets upon which the freshly delivered mothers lay, sheets still soiled and reeking from the discharges of patients who had lain on them before. It was logical to blame first the nurses for failing to send the linen to the laundry, but this he discovered immediately was unjustified. This linen had been sent to the laundry and was returned in this condition, theoretically laundered but actually not touched.

The fault lay in the common practice of administrative bureaucrats in such institutions in maintaining the various services, not at the highest quality possible, but at the lowest price. The laundry was given to a contractor who guaranteed to exchange clean bed-sheets and other linen for the soiled once a week. The bidder with the lowest price obtained the contract, with no regard to quality of laundering. As a result, for some time the laundry contractor had been carrying away bags of soiled linen and bringing back bags of so-called clean linen, sometimes without even changing the bags, and usually with little if any washing. The low price of laundering was a source of satisfaction to the administrators, but it was obvious that a high price was actually being paid—the rising rate of puerperal fever.

The evidence was incontrovertible, it lay in the stench of putrid matter which arose from the bag of linen delivered as clean by the laundry contractor, and Semmelweis took the most direct course of remedying the evil. In a cold rage he gathered up a bundle of freshly delivered sheets and stalked through the halls to the office of the director, Statthaltereirat von Tandler. Bursting into von Tandler's office unannounced he thrust his burden beneath that politician's nose, with the announcement that this "clean" linen was the cause of deaths in his department.

His radical treatment was effective, but Semmelweis made an enemy in von Tandler. Ever since there have been hospitals, administrators have been able to hamper the work of professional men at every point if they wish, so it was inevitable that there would be more trouble from this source.

Chapter 13

The Truth Rejected

WITH THE lifting in 1854 of the state of siege which had held Budapest helpless since the ill-fated revolution of 1848, and with the granting in 1856 of an amnesty to all those who had been concerned in the revolution, Budapest and all of Hungary came alive once more. The process of reconstruction began, and interest in medical science and literature increased rapidly. Von Balassa, the surgeon, now recovered from the effects of his imprisonment; Markusovsky; Hirschler, another friend of Semmelweis; and Semmelweis himself were the leaders in this movement in Budapest. The Budapest Society of Physicians was reorganized after its long period of meeting under police surveillance, and the principle of free speech in scientific discussion was emphasized. Breaking his long silence Semmelweis began the practice of discussing in this society from time to time cases of interest in his gynecological or obstetric practice. No journal was yet available to the society and these discussions were not published.

Rising in reputation and position with every year, Semmelweis began to feel at home in his native country. Hungary needed her sons, and his patriotism grew with every step he took to further his profession in Budapest. About this time, a sign of his growing content, he refused an offer from the University of Zurich of the professorship of the obstetric and gynecological clinic there. Undoubtedly he was happier than he had been for many years, possibly since the student days at Vienna, particularly because he had finally settled his attentions upon a young lady whom he planned to make his wife. Sociable, well liked, and undoubtedly, as an eligible bachelor, a target for many designing mothers and daughters, he chose now to center his attentions upon one woman, hardly more than a girl. She was quite suitable for him, however. Daughter of an excellent family, one of the group who, though planted in Hungary to aid in the Germanization of the people, had been absorbed into the native race, Marie Weidenhofer combined a fresh young beauty with a mind matured beyond her years. Her warm and generous nature, gifted with understanding, made her a perfect foil for the irascible tendencies which Semmelweis showed at times.

120

They met at the beginning of February, 1857, and were engaged by the end of the month. Through the spring Semmelweis was like another person, completely swept off his feet by the response which this young girl showed to his admiration. What difference did it make if she was but eighteen and he twenty years her senior? He was youthful in spirit, boyish in enthusiasm, and she was quiet, with a maturity belying her years. It is no wonder that they were attracted to each other, and that the attraction ripened into maturely passionate love. The wonder is that Semmelweis, he who abhorred talking, he who was sometimes shy to the point of painfulness, had managed to propose marriage.

On June 11, 1857, Ignaz Philipp Semmelweis, thirty-eight, was married to Marie Weidenhofer, eighteen. It was a gala wedding for both were popular in Budapest, especially among the younger people who did not lay so much emphasis upon the courtly social airs and graces in which Semmelweis was sometimes deficient. The couple presented a striking contrast: Semmelweis was a little bald, inclined to be portly, florid and healthy in appearance; Marie was slender, pale, her features patrician, birth and breeding in every line of her body.

The marriage began days of pleasure and peace for Semmelweis. Each day at seven in the morning he went to his clinic to examine patients and lecture to his students. He lectured chiefly in Hungarian, though the language was at that time deficient in medical nomenclature. By ten he was back at home, changed his clothes and set out to visit his private patients. His wife drove with him, reading a book while he made his calls. In the evenings they occasionally gathered about them a small circle of friends, chiefly physicians, with Markusovszky chief among them.

In the month of the marriage another venture had begun in which Semmelweis was deeply interested. The first issue of the *Orvosi Hetilap,* or Medical Weekly, had appeared with Markusovszky as its chief editor. Semmelweis came to be a contributor, forgetting his aversion to "all that is called writing" in his desire to put on record some of his interesting cases.

But the serenity of the first year of his marriage was doomed to be disturbed. Another epidemic of puerperal fever broke out in the University Clinic in the school year 1857-58. Eighteen women died.

By now, however, Semmelweis was an expert at ferreting

out these sources of infection. This time it was a nurse who had disobeyed orders. Too lazy or deliberately vindictive because of a previous rebuke, she had neglected to change the sheets after infected patients had used them.

For Semmelweis there was only one punishment for such a grievous offense, the worst he could mete out. He banished her immediately from the hospital and, had he been able, he would undoubtedly have branded her a murderess throughout the city. The woman unfortunately had some influence. There were a few objections, which Semmelweis halted summarily by threatening to expose the whole incident to the public.

Each time, it seemed, that he sought to protect the mothers who placed themselves under his care, he antagonized persons in high places. Von Tandler was his bitter enemy now, setting spies to watch for some misstep, waiting for the time when he could embarrass Semmelweis by denouncing him on a trumped-up charge. Knowing von Tandler's avid desire for facts which would put the Professor of Obstetrics in a damaging light, his spies among the students and midwives often gave him false information. Semmelweis had discovered the cause on both occasions of the outbreaks of puerperal fever in his clinic, once from the unwashed linen, and this time from the defection of the nurse, and had reported his findings in *Orvosi Hetilap*. Not knowing this, or more probably deliberately disregarding it in a desire to put Semmelweis, and also the head midwife, in a bad light, von Tandler directed to him a stern official communication, no doubt at the same time placing copies with higher authority in the ministry. This, of course, has always been a very effective device by which administrators throw professional workers employed by governments into a bad light.

As quoted in *Die Ætiologie,* the official correspondence stated:

Reports have been made confidentially, which have to do with manifold deficiencies and imperfections in the obstetrical clinic of the Imperial and Royal University, that, for example, through the negligence of the principal midwife, N. N., not only are the bedclothes of the puerperae seldom changed but even the blood-stained bedclothes of the dead puerperae were spread under newly admitted women, and as a result, the mortality at the beginning of this year, has reached such a high point, that, on one day, even ten puerperae died.

This fact must be even more shocking, since in the previous